FEISTY RIGHTY

A CANCER SURVIVOR'S JOURNEY

JENNIFER D. JAMES

This book is a work of nonfiction. Some names have been changed to respect the privacy of individuals. Descriptions, details, and characteristics of a person may have been altered. Some elements have been condensed, modified, or embellished.

This book was not written by a medical expert but as a personal memoir. The decisions, facts, explanations, and opinions contained within its pages are personal and should not be considered medical advice. If diagnosed with breast cancer, it is recommended to follow the guidance of a professional healthcare team to discuss which treatment options are best.

To my loved ones who lifted my spirits when my internal light grew dim: Bruce, Mary, Christine, David, Betty, Jerry, Ozzy, Beth, Mae, Utaiwan, and Lily. I couldn't have survived without you. Special thanks to my medical team and all the doctors, nurses, staff, and researchers, working tirelessly to help find a cure.

"And once the storm is over, you won't remember how you made it through, how you managed to survive. You won't even be sure whether the storm is really over. But one thing is certain. When you come out of the storm, you won't be the same person who walked in. That's what this storm's all about."

—Haruki Murakami

CONTENTS

PART THREE
BEYOND

AUTHOR'S NOTE

This book is based on seven handwritten journals, which document 74 medical appointments over 14 months and include my emotions, the valuable lessons I learned, the hard-fought challenges I faced, and the precious insights I've taken with me as a survivor. Detailing my breast cancer diagnosis at 41 years old, six rounds of chemotherapy, a partial mastectomy, 20 zaps of radiation, and my attempt to create a new normal, *Feisty Righty* is filled with raw honesty, hard questions, delightful realizations and emphasizes the importance of perseverance, trust, and hope.

Although extremely difficult to write (often requiring breaks when it became too emotional), this memoir is my truth. I am continually empowered by a valuable lesson that a cancer diagnosis taught me: **to live fearlessly.**

By publishing this book and increasing its outreach, I aspire to open the conversation, support breast cancer patients around the world and offer medical professionals, caregivers, and readers a window into a cancer patient's perspective.

This book is an account of my personal experience. If diagnosed with cancer, please discuss your treatment plan and health concerns with your medical team. At any point, if the content of this book feels overwhelming, please pause, and return to it when you feel ready. The healing process is different for everyone; it's important to respect and honor it.

And most importantly, I send each of you an abundance of wellness and gratitude. Just as you are now a part of my journey by reading these pages, I hope to be a valuable part of yours. Your radiant energy influences the world. Let the love of humanity and the warrior spirit within each of us shine on.

PART ONE
DISCOVERY

A TINY KITTEN

A TINY RESCUE kitten taught me what it means to be a survivor.

Sitting in the laundromat watching my clothes tumble in a dryer, I opened *Man's Search for Meaning* by Viktor E. Frankl and began to read. An autobiography about his horrific experience as a prisoner in a Nazi concentration camp during World War II, Viktor kept himself sane—and alive—by identifying his motivation and purpose. Faced with the possibility that I may not survive cancer, I, too, had begun to find some measure of comfort in discovering my life purpose.

"What's your name?" I steered my gaze from the page to a little girl who stood before me. She pulled her hand out of a potato chip bag and licked her stubby fingers clean.

Marking my page, I placed the book on my lap. "Jennifer. What's yours?"

Before she could answer, her mother called out, "Abbie, come help me hold the quarters!" and the little girl rushed over to offer her hands.

As I observed Abbie catching the coins that were spitting out of the changer like an old slot machine, an attendant arrived for her shift carrying a metal gate, litter box, two bowls, and clean blankets. Only a few feet away, she unfolded the pen, filled one of the bowls with tap water, and scooped a handful of kibble in the other. The blankets were spread out on the floor, and litter was sprinkled in the box before she left and then returned with a pet carrier.

My interest was piqued. I craned to see what was inside as she unlatched the door. Almost immediately, a tabby kitten leaped out and eagerly inspected its new surroundings. Seconds later, a skittish gray kitten cautiously followed, hunkering down by the water bowl. Both were tiny enough to fit in the palm of my hand, but the tiger-striped tabby appeared to be the runt.

It's a universal law that children are attracted to kittens, and Abbie and her little brother were no exception. With the soles of their dirty gym shoes squeaking along the floor, they ran over.

"May I hold one?" Abbie asked the attendant as she peered into the cage.

The woman smiled and shook her head. "They are too young, sweetheart. I don't think that's a good idea, but you can reach over the fence to pet them."

Unable to reach them by stretching their short arms over the metal pen, the children poked their fingers through the holes instead, sending the kittens dashing in the opposite direction. Abbie and her brother quickly lost interest and returned to their mother's side.

"They're adorable," I told the woman who took great pride in caring for them.

Completely infatuated, she said, "They're only a few weeks old. I foster cats, and there was no one at home to watch over them, so I decided to bring them to work."

I squinted and fanned my eyes as a man poured fabric softener into one of the washing machines, causing an overwhelming scent of lavender to permeate the entire room. I noticed the tiger-

striped kitten squint as well and let out a loud and
strong-willed *mew*.

"That one has a lot to say," I said and then laughed.

"He certainly does. More than her. They are siblings. The little
gray girl is much more reserved."

"Where did you find them?"

She launched into the story she'd been dying to tell. "A friend
of mine, who also fosters cats, heard the boy crying. He was
trapped behind a dumpster, caught between a concrete wall and a
wood crate. By the look of the gash in his ear and neck, he had
tried to pull himself out. We think he must have been trapped for
days. His sister was there next to him when they were rescued."

"It's good he made noise, or your friend may not have found
him."

"He has so much life in him; that's why we named him
Survivor," she said.

In that moment, I was inexplicably overcome with emotion.
As I studied Survivor—the little claws that protruded from his
paws, the whiskers that jutted from his furry cheeks, the eyes that
had adjusted to the artificial scent of a billion flowers that still
hung in the air—the gravity of his name sank in, and I felt a deep
connection to that kitten.

*As a cancer patient, I long to be a survivor, too. This tiny, wobbly-
legged, rambunctious kitten is what I want to be.*

As he bounced around on the blanket, clawing at a loose
thread while his sister stayed huddled in the corner, I wondered,
*what makes this one a survivor? Was he intelligent enough to know
that someone might hear if he cried loud and long enough? Was it the
will to live for his sister?*

"Want to take him? He's available for adoption," the attendant
asked.

Rejecting the woman's sweet offer, even though I wished I
could say yes, I told her, "Our forty-five-pound dog, Stella, rules

the house. Sharing her home with another pet wouldn't work."
But I knew in my heart Survivor would be just fine. Someone
would fall in love with his strong spirit and determination and
invite him into their family.

After folding my clean clothes, I left Survivor, his sister, and
the laundromat behind and headed home. But as I stacked my
towels on the bathroom shelf, that little kitten wouldn't leave my
thoughts. He inspired me. Sometimes life doesn't go as expected,
but the most important thing is to hold on. Survivor had tried to
free himself from the wood crate. He'd clearly experienced pain in
the process. But when he couldn't get out using his teeth and
claws, he pivoted to the other thing he had—his voice. He may
have been scared, but unlike his little gray sister, Survivor was
willing to do whatever it took to save them both.

I felt afraid of the cancer that had started to grow inside my
body. I could let the anxiety send me hunkering into the corner, or
I could, like Survivor, believe I had the power to change my future.
I had to find my voice, face fear, and persevere.

It was the only way to survive.

THE LIFE-ALTERING LUMP

ONLY 41 DAYS before I met the brave little kitten, I stood in our bathroom, sickened by a new discovery. While massaging a strained muscle in my side, my fingertips bumped into a lump in my right breast not far from my ribcage.

What is that?! I thought as I yanked my hand away.

In the next room, I could hear the muffled sound of the action movie Bruce was watching and his chuckles at whatever was unfolding onscreen. Although we were only separated by a few inches of drywall, my husband was still living in the same mundane world we'd both awoken to that day.

Out of curiosity-filled anxiety, I felt my breast again.

Oh. My. God.

I pulled my hand away, stunned, scared, and unsure of what to do next. The lump was the size of a golf ball, hard with well-defined edges. *I have breast cancer,* I immediately thought.

"It's probably nothing," I whispered to myself, hoping that hearing the words aloud might convince my intuition it was wrong. *I just need to calm down and take a shower.*

As I lathered my skin with soap, I intentionally avoided my

right breast. I didn't want to feel or touch that "thing" again. Feeling it twice, was two times, too much.

I'm being paranoid. If I have cancer, wouldn't I have other symptoms? You can't have a deadly disease and not know it, right?

Cutting the shower short, I got out, wiped the steam off the mirror, and evaluated both breasts. Everything appeared normal. Their color and shape were identical; there wasn't any redness, dimpling, or discharge from either nipple. Still, I couldn't shake the feeling that something terrible was happening inside.

As I tried to recall the events leading up to the discovery, my mind drifted back to five days earlier. While celebrating my mother-in-law's 85th birthday at a restaurant in downtown Palm Springs, I couldn't stop sneezing from seasonal allergies.

"You're starting to sound like me," Betty said, pointing her fork at me with a bite of filet mignon precariously clinging to the tines. "Once I start sneezing like that, I can't stop."

It was a relentless chain of sneezes that left my eyes watery and my nose congested.

Amidst a few annoyed glances from fellow diners, Bruce offered his cloth napkin. But before I could accept it, that familiar feeling rose back into my nose, and with another sneeze coming on, I decided to stifle it by holding my breath. What I didn't anticipate was that the stifling would do what it did—send a stabbing pain through my diaphragm.

I'd clearly pulled a muscle, but not wanting to take attention from Betty's celebration, I discretely pressed my fingers between my ribs and waited for the throbbing to subside. It finally did, at least enough to enjoy dinner, and by the time Betty blew out the candle on her slice of complimentary cake, I'd already resigned myself to the idea that I was going to have to live with the pain of a strained rib muscle for the next week or so.

I have to tell Bruce.

I opened the bathroom door slowly. Bruce was sprawled on

our bed, still engrossed in the movie. I was hoping he would notice I was upset and ask what was wrong. It felt impossible to formulate the words to tell him what had just transpired, but by answering his question, perhaps I could. I stood there with my wet hair, in my baggy pajamas and fuzzy socks, next to the television, telepathically ordering him to look at me.

Notice me. NOTICE me.

But to Bruce, it was still an ordinary watch-some-television-before-bed kind of night. The only sirens that sounded were the ones on TV. He just chuckled again at whatever corny joke the actor made.

Impatient, I worked up the nerve and finally said, "I found a lump!"

Bruce looked at me, confused. "You found what?" He grabbed the remote and hit pause right when a car had been blown to bits on the screen. A tire here. A bumper there. Flames froze within a cloud of smoke, which felt strangely symbolic as my world had just exploded, too.

"I-I-I can't believe it," I stuttered, pacing like a tiger confined inside a cage. Fear and frenzy overtook me as I started rambling, "How can this be? Why is this happening?"

And finally, he asked, "Where is it in your breast?"

My palm hovered over the area, careful not to touch it. He was silent. I was silent. And within seconds, that silence became so unbearable that I asked him if he wanted to feel it.

"No!" His response was quick—*too quick*—as if whatever lurked inside was some vicious and evil thing that might attack him next.

"What am I going to do?" I frantically blurted out.

"Try not to worry," he said. "Why don't you contact your doctor to see if you can get in to have it checked?" His words were logical, and his voice was calm and steady.

Yes, that's what I'll do. I'll contact Dr. Scott.

I rushed into my office to compose an email. If there was a slight possibility she was in her office at 9:00 p.m. on a Sunday, I would have driven the two hours from Palm Springs to Los Angeles in my pajamas to get an answer.

With trembling fingers, I typed:

Dear Dr. Scott,

I found a lump in my right breast. It's close to the nipple, and when I press down on it, it feels like it affects my back and shoulder blade muscles. Would it be possible for me to come in and have it checked? I would feel much better getting your professional advice in case it's something serious.

Best,

Jennifer

Hitting the send button, I had successfully heaved that crushing weight into her court, which brought an iota of peace. My plea was at the top of her emails, in bold, begging to be read.

Relax and try to get some sleep, I thought.

I remembered my mother's words from my childhood days, "Just lie still," she would say as she steered me out of my parents' bedroom and back to my own. "Your body needs rest. Just lie still. It will help." She knew, eventually, sleep would come.

I woke up to daylight peeking its way through the slats of our blinds and doves cooing outside. For a moment, everything seemed normal. But before I could sit up, the thought of the lump screeched into my morning reality. Kicking the covers off, I rushed into the office to check for an email.

At 6:00 a.m., Dr. Scott had not responded. *What if she's out on vacation or away at a medical conference and won't be back for days?* I trusted Dr. Scott. She held the power to dissipate the cloud of fear that hovered over me.

Trying not to overthink, *even though I am quite an expert at overthinking,* I made coffee and toasted a few slices of sourdough but spilled the creamer and burnt the bread. Unable to concentrate on even the simplest tasks, I turned on the local news. Murders and robberies were equally as depressing. By 8:00 a.m., it was time to take matters into my own hands, so proactively, I dialed Dr. Scott's office number.

The medical operator asked, "Are you calling to make an appointment with Dr. Scott?"

"Yes!"

"Is this an emergency?"

The truth was, I had no idea whether this was an emergency or not. It wasn't as if I had been shot in the chest, but yes, this could be a matter of life and death.

"Sort of," I stammered. "It's not a 9-1-1 type of emergency, but it's super important that I see her immediately."

"So, what's the reason for the visit?"

"I found...," but the words were stuck in my throat.

"Ma'am?"

With a few deep breaths, "I found a lump in my right breast," eventually escaped.

I could hear the clicking of the keyboard, followed by, "The soonest I can get you in is on the morning of April thirteenth."

Three days away? There is no way I can wait that long.

"I have a lump in my breast that needs to be checked out immediately," I said, hoping to better convey the urgency.

"Okay," and then there was a significant pause. "Should I set up the appointment for the thirteenth?"

"Um, yeah!" I didn't intend for it to sound sarcastic, but damn, this was important. Couldn't she see that?

With the appointment made, I hung up, hoping Dr. Scott would soon see my email and respond directly. While trying to focus on writing contracts for work, I kept the online medical portal refreshed, checking it repeatedly.

Ten minutes passed, *nothing.*

Thirty minutes, *nothing.*

Forty-five minutes, *still nothing.*

Sixty nerve-racking minutes later, an email from Dr. Scott's nurse read, WE'LL SEE YOU AT 10:00 A.M. ON THE THIRTEENTH.

Seventy-two hours of pure anxiety. Seventy-two hours of temporary insanity. I have no idea how I'll get through the next 72 hours.

I hoped my older sister could provide some clarity. In our lifetimes, whenever I became consumed with emotion, she leaned on logic. Plus, she's the type of woman who punches a problem in the face. I needed my problem punched.

"I doubt it's cancer," Chris told me over the phone. "Besides that, didn't you just have a mammogram?"

"Yes, about nine months ago. The letter I received in the mail said that I have dense breast tissue, but everything appeared normal," I explained.

"Mammograms are supposed to detect cancer. The odds are pretty good it would have spotted a tumor."

"True, but the lump I felt is as big as a golf ball. If it wasn't there then, and it's there now, what does that mean? Is this cancer fast-growing and super aggressive?"

"Just try to remain calm," she said, "and go clean something." After being siblings for over 40 years, she knew me well.

When I was stressed or when something bad happened, I kept myself busy in order to burn off the nervous energy. We repainted the studio floor and walls when Bruce's father passed away. When my dad was undergoing quadruple bypass heart surgery back in Nebraska, I went outside to wash and detail our cars. The only way to survive the wait was to stay busy to the point of physical exhaustion. By the time I finished that day, there wasn't a single speck of dust, fingerprint, or errant crumb anywhere in our three-bedroom house.

After 19 years together, married for 12, Bruce and I had been through this level of chaos before. We had an unspoken rule for dealing with it: don't think, do. We didn't discuss our anxiety, but when one of our productivity levels shot through the roof, the other automatically knew.

Bombarded by the smell of furniture wax as he walked into the room, Bruce asked with a knowing smile, "Been cleaning a lot?"

"Going to organize my closet and sock drawer next," I said, waving a rag in my hand and hoping there were enough projects left to keep me occupied.

AN EPIPHANY AT SIX

EVEN THOUGH I had no proof that my lump was cancerous, the fear that it was, crept into everything I did.

Stella needs her walk. *What if I have cancer?*

Did I make the car payment this month? *What if I have cancer?*

"Bruce, would you like Indian food for dinner?" *What if I have cancer? What if I have cancer? What if I have cancer?*

The fear wouldn't leave me alone.

On April 13, it was finally time to unravel the mystery and identify the lump in my right breast. The two-hour drive from Palm Springs to Dr. Scott's office in Los Angeles was complete anxiety. As I sat in traffic, I flipped through my music playlist, repeatedly adjusted side mirrors, pulled the visor down, pushed the visor up, and tried to think about *anything* but the lump. Thoughts about our recent relocation seemed to help.

Two months earlier, we moved from our L.A. loft to our weekend house in Palm Springs. As much as I loved being closer to Bruce's aging mother and appreciated the sounds of nature over the incessant din of cars on the freeway, there were things I missed after a 17-year stint in the big city. The pace and energy drew me in, as did the convenience of finding anything I wanted within a five-minute walk. It helped that I still had attachments to Los Angeles. Our photo shoots, for the most part, still took place there. My mom and sister both lived in the South Bay, a cluster of beach cities nestled in the southwest corner of L.A. County. And, of course, I kept Dr. Scott as my primary care physician, not only because I thought she was an excellent doctor but because it was an additional thread that kept me connected.

I pulled into the last parking spot and rushed into the medical building for my appointment. After I checked in, I waited—*impatiently*—for a nurse to call my name.

Sitting on the exam table in one of Dr. Scott's rooms, fidgeting with the ties of the faded medical gown, I tried to minimize my anxiety by thinking positively. *I am young and healthy; I will be fine. Nine months ago, I had a clean and clear mammogram. That's significant.* But as quickly as the positive thoughts formed, they were forced out by doubt. *If a woman can gestate a human in nine months, it certainly could grow a deadly tumor, right?*

Prefaced by a firm knock on the door, Dr. Scott peeked in. Brilliant, warm, and caring, I immediately felt protected when she entered the room. Usually, we'd start an appointment by discussing upcoming travel plans or new restaurants, but this time, casual conversation wasn't appropriate.

She had me lie back as she examined my right breast thoroughly, pressing her fingertips systematically over every inch. I tried to read her expression, waiting for her to clench her jaw or furrow her brow if she felt something odd. Her reaction would confirm that the lump was serious. If she didn't, maybe I'd overreacted. But her face remained expressionless, giving nothing away.

Once she had finished examining both breasts, she lowered herself onto her stool, still stoic. "I felt something, too. Women get lumps in their breasts, and often, it's nothing. I'm going to call the women's clinic to see if they can get you back in for a mammogram today. Go ahead and get dressed and meet me in the hall." When I opened the door, she was waiting. "Go there now," she said in a more serious tone than I'd ever heard from her before.

I knew it, I thought. *It's something.*

I sped through three yellow lights on my drive to the women's clinic, a few miles away. After a series of X-ray captures, the mammography tech picked up the phone and called an on-site doctor. Nine months ago, I'd waited a week for a letter to arrive with the results. This time, it was less than five minutes. Their urgency was, in some ways, a relief, but it simultaneously confirmed that I was facing something serious enough that immediacy counts.

When the doctor introduced herself, I was in such distress I never caught her name, so I'll refer to her as Dr. Nameless. She pored over the images on a monitor across the room. But just like Dr. Scott, her expression didn't falter.

"I'd like you to get a biopsy done so we can remove some cells and test them," she finally said as she sat in a chair opposite me.

Test them for what? She purposely didn't use the "C" word. I wanted her to declare the disease by its name. It was as if she had buried the most important reason why I was there.

But Dr. Nameless took a different approach, detailing what to expect during the biopsy. Within seconds of listening, my nervous system went into overload. All I heard was a loud, amplified buzz. Certain words interrupted the static: lie on your back ... *zzz* ... abnormal ... *zzz* ... anesthesia ... *zzz* ... and then, tiny incision. With so many gaps, it was impossible to weave them together.

In a distorted voice that sounded as if she was underwater, I finally heard her ask, "Do you have any questions?"

I wanted to say, "I have a million. Please start over and explain everything again," but I didn't. I just shook my head as if I had comprehended every word.

"I've scheduled the biopsy for April twenty-eighth," she continued. "Does that work for you?"

Fifteen days? I could barely survive the past 72 hours. I wanted to plead with her to get me in sooner, to give me the answer I needed before going completely crazy, but I didn't ask to change it (mostly because I had forgotten how to form sentences).

On my drive home, new thoughts fought for space in my crammed-to-the-brim brain. *What if the biopsy hurts? What if I have cancer and can no longer work? What if not working affects us financially? What if I die?*

Seriously, what if I die?

Even though thousands of cars surrounded me on the 10 freeway, I felt isolated and alone. It took me back to when I was six, sitting cross-legged in my childhood bedroom with a doll. I'd had an eye-opening epiphany while brushing my Barbie's hair.

The emotions and the thoughts I experience do not belong to anyone else. They begin and end with me. And then, *someday, I will have to face death alone.*

The revelation was so powerful, so mature, that I could no longer play. Before then, I believed my mom, sister, and father experienced life as one. We functioned with one set of emotions. One set of feelings. One collection of thoughts. Terrified, I ran downstairs to the kitchen to find my mom. That day, she hugged the fear of dying out of me.

By the time I pulled into the driveway of our Palm Springs home two hours later, the thought of having cancer had become an impenetrable brick wall that towered over me and blocked out the sunlight. I felt like I had stepped into a shadow, and no matter where I went, the shadow remained. It was the shadow of something big, about to change my life forever.

What if I never see the sun again? What if I am stuck in the darkness forever? What if that darkness is cancer?

And even though I knew I had an amazing support team to help me through whatever was coming, this giant obstacle was something I'd have to face alone. No amount of positivity could change that fact. This was my fear to face, my challenge to overcome, and I'd have to find a way, somehow, to conquer it.

2,399 OTHER WOMEN

THERE'S REGULAR TIME, and then there's the 'waiting-to-find-out-if-you-have-cancer time,' which moves at such a sluggish pace you have every opportunity to dream up dreadful scenarios. During the 15 days I waited to get my biopsy, I died of cancer over one thousand times ... at least in my mind.

"Jennifer," a nurse called out, "we are ready for you." I got up, leaving Bruce behind in the waiting room, clenching the back of my gown closed to hide my undies.

"I'll be right here," Bruce assured me as he looked up from the magazine he was reading. "Good luck!"

As I entered the biopsy room, I first noticed the surgical tools lined up on a metal tray, shiny, ready, and sterile. On a computer stand sat an ultrasound wand accompanied by a monitor with a screensaver depicting a secluded, white-sand beach. At one time, the image would have provided tranquility. But in my current mental condition, it actually heightened the anxiety of feeling stuck.

The nurse helped me onto the biopsy table, "You can lie down on your back," she told me, adding a few more surgical tools to the tray.

As previously instructed, I had come prepared. I arrived with clean skin and deodorant-free armpits, which were now sticky with sweat. I hadn't taken blood thinners, vitamins, or supplements for seven days, and I brought a bra with firm support to put on afterward. Every box listed on the "How to Prepare for a Biopsy" paperwork was checked.

"I am terrified about all of this," I confessed, hoping that talking might help release my abundance of nervous energy.

"It's understandable," she said, sending the island scene away with a click of her mouse, "but statistically, about eighty to eighty-five percent of breast lumps are benign."

How did I not know that the odds are stacked in my favor?

As optimistic as it sounded, the statistics couldn't assuage the uneasy feeling in my gut that something was terribly wrong. Even without any physical pain or discomfort, my instincts were sounding alarm bells, trying to protect me.

"How many biopsies do you perform here in a single day?" I asked as she placed the cold ultrasound wand on my breast.

"Our facility does ten ultrasound-guided core biopsies daily, Monday through Friday."

Fifty per week! 200 per month ... 2,400 each year in only one facility ... in one city ... in one country ... and that's only one type of breast biopsy. At a benign rate of 80 percent, 1,920 women are in the clear, leaving 480 women who aren't.

The numbers were both daunting and comforting. If my results came back with cancer, I was in the company of 479 other women who could empathize, first-hand, with what I was going through.

Dr. Nameless had explained the test in detail, but my mind had been, well, incapable of processing the information, so I asked, "How is this biopsy different than others?"

"Today, we will extract cells from the abnormal mass to determine if cancer cells are inside," she explained.

Did she just use the "C" word?

I felt supported. It was empowering to hear the nurse use the actual word, knowing how Dr. Scott and Dr. Nameless avoided saying it. I knew why I was there. She knew why I was there. By acknowledging it, she seemed ready to attack it if necessary.

A few minutes later, through the closed door, I heard high heels clicking along the tile floor in the hallway. They stopped, and a moment later, in walked Dr. Fez. Her white coat hung open, revealing a tailored designer dress underneath. Despite her penchant for fashion, just like the other doctors who wore khakis and sneakers, she had an intense focus and let's-get-this-done attitude. After a quick introduction, she went straight to work.

"I'm going to numb the area first," she informed me and picked up an injection needle. There was a small prick and a pinch. Within minutes, the rest of my body felt separated from Righty as part of my breast became numb. "Now I'm going to make a small incision," she said, picking up a hollow needle with a tip the size of a sharpened pencil. "I'll extract tissue samples from different parts of the abnormal mass."

At first, the mild discomfort was tolerable, but when she pressed harder into the mass, I felt a sharp pain. Steadying my body so it wouldn't move, I tightened my muscles to press against it. With each sample, the pain intensified.

Take control. Just get through this, I told myself.

To prevent myself from passing out, I shifted my focus to my Grandma Wells. Grandma Wells was my maternal grandmother, and as kids, Chris and I spent the summers running through the sprinklers behind her boxy, one-bedroom home in a sleepy little town in rural Nebraska. She was a chubby five-foot-tall firecracker of a woman who, at 18, married my grandfather. Together they survived everything from the Great Depression to raising four children. She made the best blueberry pie and popcorn balls, and when she wasn't gardening or reading books to us or playing a game she loved called "A Hundred Ways to Get There," she worked part-time at the local library. Although she had passed away years ago, thinking about her always helped me to relax.

Grandma, it hurts, I said in silence.

Her presence immediately connected with mine. At the foot of the biopsy table, I saw her appear. She was exactly as I remembered, with short grey-permed hair and bifocals that magnified her green eyes, and she was dressed in a navy polyester pantsuit and matching blouse. A trace of her *Lily of the Valley* perfume drifted through the air, fresh and sweet, as if a bouquet had been delivered to the biopsy room.

And then her words came to me, "It's not as bad as a bone marrow test," which made me smile.

The horror of that test was actually a running joke in our family. Grandma had been advised by her doctor to have one, and it was apparently more painful than she had anticipated. From then on, she was adamant about never going through it again.

She'd warn her grandchildren, "If a doctor ever tries to persuade you to get one, refuse!" So the bone marrow test became the 'pain standard' that every other uncomfortable experience was compared to.

"I have to get all four of my wisdom teeth pulled," Chris had lamented on her first summer home from college.

Grandma responded, "It won't hurt as bad as a bone marrow test."

Lying on her couch, sick with the flu, I'd muttered, "I can't stop barfing."

"Barfing isn't as bad as a bone marrow test," she replied, heading into the kitchen to make me hot tea and toast.

When I was a teenager, Grandma moved into a 65 and over apartment complex that was down the street from my high school. Occasionally, I'd walk there and spend the afternoons with her, watching black-and-white westerns on her old tube television, situated inside an even older mahogany cabinet.

"I got a 'D' in Geometry, and Mom is going to kill me," I told her.

"Getting killed won't hurt half as bad as a bone marrow test," she said, looking up with a smirk. We both laughed hysterically.

"I'm finished." Dr. Fez interrupted. She peeled off sticky labels —printed with my name and medical number—and wrapped them around each sample tube. "The cut was very tiny, so no stitches are required. I'll call you in five days with the results." At the moment she finished her sentence, Grandma vanished.

The nurse picked up where the doctor left off by applying pressure to the incision. "It's normal to experience bruising or tenderness afterward. Do not take any blood thinners for a few days and avoid working out for the remainder of the day."

No problem, I thought. Unless you count my daily dog walks with Stella, I wasn't someone who worked out, and I planned on going home and doing nothing more than curling up on the sofa and watching an episode of *Say Yes to the Dress* while dreaming about my sister's upcoming wedding.

Next spring, my sister and David would say, "I do" in Jamaica, surrounded by family and close friends. As her Matron of Honor, I considered the television show to be "research" and a worthy use of time during my recovery.

"One more thing," the nurse added, almost as an afterthought. "You now have a small metal clip inside of your breast. It's placed there so your medical team can pinpoint where the biopsy occurred."

Once she carefully covered the incision with a thick pad and taped it into position, she helped me off the table, reminding me that I'd get the results in five days.

As I began to walk back to the dressing room, I noticed that every movement, every step, sent a sharp pain through my breast. Trying to minimize the 'bounce,' I scooted my feet slowly over the carpet like a cross-country skier. It looked odd, but I didn't care. I'd endured enough for one day.

When I returned to the waiting room, Bruce was sitting in the same spot. "Why are you walking like that?" he asked.

"It's the Boob Biopsy Shuffle," I said half-sarcastically as I clenched my teeth in pain. Although we were alone, if one of those other 2,399 women had been sitting there, I would've warned her that the way she walked into the biopsy room would be very different than the way she walked out.

In the car, leaving the parking structure, I noticed an ungodly number of speed bumps that I could've sworn weren't there when I arrived an hour earlier. I groaned in pain as our Prius thumped over the first one. Bruce slowed down over the second, but it didn't help. When we came to the last one, he barely accelerated, and the car slid back.

As he pressed harder on the gas pedal, he joked, "If we go any slower, we'll start moving backward."

I couldn't help but think that going backward wouldn't be so bad. I would have loved to have gone back in time to the days before my lump began to grow. Back when doctor appointments happened only once a year, and my mind volleyed from thought to thought without questions of mortality lurking behind each and every one. But that's what makes life tricky. You don't always get what you want. There *is* no going back. Like the 2,399 other women, who had, or soon would, walk out the clinic's doors with the same shuffle, I had no choice but to keep shufflin'.

MAYDAY ON THE FIRST
OF MAY

WHEN MY PHONE RANG, we were speeding down the freeway with a pickup bed full of photography equipment en route to a studio in Los Angeles. Bruce turned down the radio so I could answer, but I didn't recognize the number and told him I'd let it go to voicemail.

"Maybe it's a client," he replied.

"Or a sales call," I said, fully committed to not answering.

"You should pick up."

"Really?"

"You should." He was adamant, so I answered.

"Jennifer, it's Dr. Fez." Hearing her voice surprised me. It had only been two full days since the biopsy, not five. "I have some difficult news to share," she said in a painstakingly professional tone. "They found cancer cells in the tissue."

Then there was silence. She waited for me to process the information. As her words sank in, and I realized she wasn't going to say anything more, my brain went into panic mode.

Help! Mayday! Mayday! This is an emergency! Change this outcome right now! It was a desperate plea for help.

"Jennifer?" Dr. Fez needed a response, but I couldn't talk. All I could sense was the heavy pounding of my heart in my chest and the sting of tears forming in my eyes. "I am so sorry to share this news with you," she finally said.

And then it felt as if the floor fell out from beneath me as I dropped into a pool of darkness. My mind frantically searched for other possibilities. *It's a mistake. Maybe the samples they tested were accidentally switched.* But I'd watched Dr. Fez label the tubes with my name and medical number.

They. Were. Mine.

My instincts had tried to prepare me for this moment, but I was in no way prepared. Despite being plagued with constant thoughts of cancer from the moment I felt the lump to when the doctor told me definitively that I had it, I was blindsided.

"I'd like to have you get a targeted mammogram done so we can document the status," she said, trying to move the conversation forward.

"Who is it?" Bruce asked, quickly glancing over at me. I pressed my hand over my left ear to block out any distractions that would prevent me from hearing what Dr. Fez had to say.

"It will help us decide the best way to proceed," she added.

I murmured, "Thank you," politely as if my entire existence hadn't just crumbled.

"I'll have someone on my team call to set it up." It was the last thing she said before she hung up.

I sat in the passenger seat of the car and pretended to remain on the call for a few more minutes to give myself time. When I finally placed the phone in my lap, Bruce glanced over again.

"What's wrong?" he asked, now worried. I hunkered down in my seat, waiting for my thoughts to stop reeling. "Tell me what's wrong."

I mouthed the words, *I have cancer,* without looking up.

"Please, tell me. What's going on?"

In a shaky, barely audible voice that didn't feel like it was coming from me, I heard myself say the words, "I have breast cancer."

Bruce reflexively hit the brakes. With a squeal of the tires, photography equipment slammed into the cab's back wall with a jolt. Realizing what he'd done, he whipped his head around to see if he could change lanes, then steered the pickup off the freeway and down the exit ramp. The first parking lot he saw, he pulled in and stopped.

For a full ten minutes, we hugged each other and cried. When I finally lifted my head from his chest and looked through the windshield, everything in the outside world appeared blurry, as if there were torrential rains and the wipers couldn't keep up.

Out the side window, cars were lined up at a fast-food drive-through. Although I couldn't see the drivers, I knew they were all mundanely staring at a menu board, deciding what to order for lunch. Jealousy shot through me. I wanted my biggest concern to be whether I should order a cheeseburger or a chicken sandwich. Their lives were still normal. Now, for me, everything had changed.

There are stories about near-death experiences where a person's perspective shifts from inside their body to outside. That afternoon, for the first time, I ascended to a different plane. High above, with a birds-eye view, I floated in a chalky blue sky. I could see our pickup. I could see us hugging. Cars weaved around the truck without a sound. The only noise I could hear was the soughing of the wind as it rustled the leaves of some oak trees. It was as if I had transitioned to another dimension, one between life and death.

Several minutes passed before Bruce was able to catch a full breath of air. He then uttered, "I can't believe it. What do we do now?"

Attempting to be strong and take control of a situation neither of us could control, I stated the obvious, "We have to drop the equipment off at the studio for tomorrow's shoot."

"But how?" he asked. I knew what he meant. How do we pretend everything is okay when it isn't?

"We'll get through it," I said. "But after that, I need to go to my mom's and tell her." My mother knew about the lump and how eager I was to find out what it was.

As he started the truck's engine and pulled back onto the busy freeway, I thought about the concept of time. Some dates are significant enough that you never forget the moment, such as births, deaths, marriages, and graduations. May 1, 2017, was the day I was diagnosed with Invasive Ductal Carcinoma. And I knew then it would scar my memory forever.

If I can make it to the end of this year, I thought, *it'll be a miracle.*

WHY NOT ME?

My blood pressure always spiked when I went to the doctor. Any doctor, for any reason. One step inside a medical office and my heart would race, and I'd get clammy from the surge of adrenaline. Those lifeless blue walls, combined with the smell of antiseptic, sent my fight-or-flight response into overdrive.

"You have White Coat Hypertension," Dr. Scott informed me during an annual physical several years before my diagnosis. "It's common. About twenty percent of the people who see me have it."

I hope she understood it wasn't personal. I liked Dr. Scott a lot; but I probably would've liked her more if our encounters didn't involve her wearing a lab coat and me wearing a medical gown.

As she wrapped the blood pressure cuff around my arm for the third time in 15 minutes, knowing my blood pressure would eventually drop within a normal range, she looked up at me and asked, "What are you scared of getting?"

Without thinking, I'd blurted out, "I'm scared you're going to tell me I have cancer."

29

She grinned, cocked her head, and replied, "That's funny; I'm scared of getting dementia."

By the time she typed up the appointment summary, I was still surprised that I'd had such a quick and adamant answer to her question. No one had ever asked me that before. After that terrible call from Dr. Fez letting me know that my worst night-mare had come true, I couldn't help but wonder if my diagnosis was a self-fulfilling prophecy. Had my deeply-rooted fear somehow caused it to actually happen? Or was I getting subtle signals from my intuition for years prior?

Even more concerning, could my getting cancer be karma playing out? In seventh grade, I made fun of a classmate for having acne. Did I get cancer from being mean? In middle school, I triggered the fire alarm so my friends and I could cut class. In college, I left a bar without paying the tab. But surely, everyone has done something stupid in their youth that they regret, right? In short, could I have somehow prevented this from happening if I'd just been a better person? Most doctors would tell you no; cells become malignant due to a myriad of biological and environ-mental reasons, none of them having to do with karma. But when diagnosed, you can't help but wonder, *why me?*

Why me?

Only an hour or so after hearing from Dr. Fez that cancer was growing inside me, Bruce and I pulled into the studio parking lot to drop off the photo equipment, and by then, I had asked the puzzling question a dozen times. When our friend who owned the building let us in, we pretended to be too busy to chat.

We unloaded the equipment at a record speed, dumping off c-stands, strobe packs, grip cases, and lights without setting up or unpacking anything. We needed to get out of there before anyone questioned why our eyes were puffy from crying and why we were too distracted to speak.

On our way to my mother's condominium, I silently repeated

the same ambiguous question. *Why me?* I needed to know the answer to rationalize why my luck had turned bad.

Why ME?

But finally, a clear message entered my mind. I didn't know if the voice came from the Universe or God or if it was the tiny voice of reason hidden deep within my frontal lobe where rational thought is born, but the message was undeniable.

I heard the response:

Why NOT you?

Stunned, I didn't know how to react. Yes. Why NOT me? Of course, bad things happen, even to good people. Cancer happened to my Uncle Don, Uncle Gary, Cousin Tammy, Bruce's brother, and my friend, Krista. If it can happen to them, why couldn't it happen to me?

* * *

When we pulled into the parking garage of my mom's complex, I was terrified, knowing I was about to upturn her life. Climbing the stairs to her front door, it was as if my shoes were weighted with rocks. I placed my hand on the doorknob, but when it came to turning it to go inside, I couldn't.

Bruce stopped behind me on the landing. "What's wrong?"

I peeked through the slatted blinds of my mom's window to see her sitting on the sofa, chatting on the phone, smiling, and still living in a world where her daughter was healthy.

I whispered back, "I'm not sure I'll be able to tell her."

I didn't want to see my mother's expression when I verbalized the news. But beyond that, without enough time to fully process the diagnosis myself, I didn't want to say the words. The more I uttered them, the closer I'd get to having to accept them. I wasn't ready to do that.

Bruce squeezed past me and opened the door. I could hear her say over the low rumbling of the dryer, "How many pages were you able to write today?" I knew by the question she was talking to my older sister, a professional screenwriter.

When my mom saw how upset we both looked, she jumped to her feet and rushed over. "What's going on?" she asked with the receiver still pressed against her ear. "Tell me what happened."

Tears were unleashed before I could say, "I have breast cancer."

"I am so sorry. Honey, I am so terribly sorry."

My sister's voice was faint as it echoed through the receiver, "Mom, what's going on?" When my mother didn't respond to her question, she became frantic. "Mom, what's going on?!"

"Jennifer's been diagnosed with cancer. Christine, I have to let you go." She ended the call and dropped the phone onto the sofa.

"I can't believe it," I cried as I sunk into her arms.

When my mom tried to pull away to look me in the eyes, I wouldn't let her go. Instead, I held on tighter as if she were my life preserver. To me, she had superpowers that only a mom could use, like when she pulled loose gravel from my bloody elbow after a bike accident and when she talked me through a middle-school breakup after my first love cheated.

Do it again, Mom, I thought. *Use your powers!*

"I feel like the outcome will be good. Everything will be okay," she finally said. Her voice seemed solid as she rubbed her palm over my back. I wondered if she believed it herself or if it was something she knew I needed to hear.

I looked past my mother's shoulder to scan the room for Bruce. He was out on the balcony, staring up at the sky in disbelief. Unsure of what he should say or how to act, it was best to pass the difficult situation back to the woman who had brought his wife into the world even though there was nothing she could do either, and we all knew it.

We heard my sister's footsteps pounding up the outside stairs

32

a few minutes later. As if she was coming to save us from a burning building, the door flew open, and she rushed in.

"Sis, what happened?" she asked. Although she had heard it over the phone, she had to hear it from me to believe it.

I had accumulated so much air in my lungs from sobbing I could barely speak. With a long exhale, I told her, "I have breast cancer."

I let go of my mother, collapsing in my sister's arms. I could feel her muscles contract as she tried to hold my weight. Chris wasn't only physically strong but intelligent, determined, and knew how to problem-solve.

A few inches taller than me, she hunched down to eye level, and with the same conviction she would tell someone to trust her with a ten-million-dollar film budget, she said, "Sis, we're going to kick cancer's ass. We'll do it together."

I knew she meant it. My sister lived by the phrase, "Say what you mean and mean what you say." It was her mantra. Extremely honest, she would never tell someone a lie to save their feelings. So, when it came to fighting something as serious as cancer, I knew she believed it.

Without any tears left to cry, it felt as if the brunt of the storm had passed. As I sat exhausted in the rubble of my new reality, my sister called David, her fiancé, to let him know what had transpired.

I looked around the room at each of them, grateful that my mom and sister lived nearby. After only six hours of being a cancer patient, I realized it would take a village of support to help pull me through. My village started with a population of three and with David, four.

We sat down at the dining room table for dinner. Without an appetite, I couldn't help but think about the next day's photo shoot. I wasn't ready to tell our clients and crew about the diagnosis and wasn't sure if I ever wanted them to know. *How will they NOT know by the way we look and act?*

Somewhere between putting a spoonful of baby carrots on my plate and buttering a piece of bread, like a phoenix rising from the ash, another unsolicited message from deep within me popped into my brain.

This time it said:

Journal the experience.

I didn't know why. I just knew I'd been tasked with an obligation I had to fulfill. An assignment. That the experience had to be documented for some unknown reason.

To signify my acknowledgment, I announced to my family, "I am going to journal my experience daily."

My mom showed her usual flood of support. "That's a fantastic idea. It could really help others going through the same situation."

"Writing can be therapeutic," my sister added. "I think you should."

Bruce looked up and grinned, so I knew he had heard what I said. But instead of commenting on the idea, he, in his typical off-beat way, asked, "Mom, can you pass the mashed potatoes?" It made us all smile as she handed him the serving bowl.

I may never know the exact reason why I got cancer. Destiny has a way of surprising us without an explanation. As much as we want to skip through life by experiencing as few hardships as possible, the hardships are inevitable.

My Grandma Wells always said, "It takes the bad stuff to make us appreciate the good." And at that moment, I appreciated my cancer-free past more than ever.

NIGHTLY SHOCKWAVES

THREE DAYS after the life-changing call from Dr. Fez, I sat alone during my targeted mammogram, waiting, as I clenched my medical gown closed. My life felt unfamiliar as if I no longer had any control over, well, anything. All I could do was wait.

Wait for the mammographer to return.

Wait to meet the doctor.

Wait to become cancer-free again.

Several minutes later, the mammographer returned and apologized to me that the doctor had requested more angles. After eight more rounds of "breathe" and "don't breathe," listening for the machine's high-pitched beep before telling me I could "breathe" again, she rushed back out of the room for additional feedback.

I sat alone, *again,* waiting.

When the door swung open, and a new doctor appeared, I had hope that she was the one. *This will be the doctor who will cross the sea of cancer to rescue me,* I thought. *This is her.*

But I quickly changed my mind when she handed me a booklet with the title—*What is Breast Cancer?* "I'm Dr. Myers. I think this might help you learn more about your situation," she said.

Now, I'm sure the delivery of the book was proper protocol, and I respected the fact that she was efficiently doing her job, but at the same time, the idea that she felt I needed a booklet to explain cancer seemed, in an odd way, condescending.

Everyone knows what cancer is, don't they? It's the same disease that had stolen the life of my dear friend Krista only two months before. And my uncle a few years before that. It had taken my Grandpa Wells before I was born, robbing me of my chance to meet him. Even as I sat there, Bruce's brother was in the middle of his own fight against colon cancer. *So, yes, Dr. Myers. I know what cancer is. I'm quite familiar.*

* * *

When I got home, I tucked the booklet inside a cabinet with no real intention of reading it. Since it was given to me by a doctor, it seemed too important to throw away, and yet, leaving it out in the open would serve as another reminder of my disease. Beyond that, it might haunt my thoughts—or even my dreams—like some disturbing crime novel containing graphic photographs with explicit descriptions.

But then again, I hadn't slept much anyway.

Ever since my diagnosis, I'd wake up in the middle of the night, often numerous times, with my heart racing and my pajamas soaked in sweat. These anxiety attacks happened so frequently that I actually named the condition.

Already knowing the answer, Bruce would ask, "Did you sleep okay last night?"

"Oh, just another round of *Nightly Shockwaves*," I'd grumble as I made an extra large cup of coffee to combat the exhaustion.

My insomnia went something like this:

At approximately 2:30 a.m., my eyes would pop open. *Oh shit! I have cancer!* After thirty minutes, I'd eventually fall back to sleep.

At 3:40 a.m., it would strike again, causing me to bolt up in bed. *Oh shit! I have cancer!*

And then another shock would happen around 5:15 a.m., which at that time, I'd think, *I might as well get up,* and I'd drag myself out of bed to formally end my ineffective sleep cycle until 10:00 p.m. that night when it would start all over.

Although I knew it was the fear of cancer interrupting my circadian rhythm, I laid blame on anything but. Irritable and feeling utterly sorry for myself, it was easier to be angry at the external noises that happened. Being awakened by an annoying sound was familiar. Having cancer wasn't.

Damn the chirping crickets.

Damn the leaky faucet.

Damn the stormy weather.

My sleep was so fragile and unsettled that the faintest noise, like Stella slurping water from her bowl in the kitchen, could yank me out of my fidgety slumber. And right afterward came the guilt.

How can I expect my immune system to combat cancer if I am this sleep-deprived?

Between the waiting, the blame, and the guilt, it didn't take long before I was on the verge of self-destruction. Caught up in another round of *Nightly Shockwaves,* I had to take action. If I wanted to assist my body in becoming cancer-free, I needed to find a way to take back some control.

Instead of allowing my mind to overthink, I decided to focus on the cool pillowcase beneath my cheek. Instead of feeling discouraged about my future, I concentrated on the weight of our blanket on my body. Instead of worrying about how severe my cancer was, I listened to the sound of my breath, traveling in and out of my lungs.

Most nights, it worked, and the *Nightly Shockwaves* subsided.

Like ocean waves that relentlessly batter the shore, the tide eventually calms with the ebb of the current. Snuggling into the present, I found a way past the choppiness to a place where the placid surface gently rises and falls.

To get there each night, I reminded myself:

At this moment, you are alive, and no other moment exists.

THE SECRET SOCIETY

Even though I was able to get a better handle on the *Nightly Shockwaves*, during the day, cancer stayed on my mind. And yet, at the same time, I didn't want to acknowledge that I even had it. Since the diagnosis, I hadn't touched or looked at my right breast. To touch or look would somehow make it all the more real.

In order to fully accept that a problem exists, we must face it. If there's a fire, we don't turn our backs. Acknowledging the problem is the first step in overcoming it.

It was time to look.

As I stood in the shower, engulfed in a cloud of steam that I hoped would obscure my hard-to-accept reality, I forced my chin down and opened my eyes to take a peek at my right breast. *What the...* I immediately jerked my head back, gasped, and looked up.

Big. Mistake.

My skin was severely bruised from the targeted mammogram with deep purplish-black marks that were caused by repeated squishing, squeezing, and pulling. Even though the marks were shocking to see, they were made by the good guys. Collateral damage as they tried to pinpoint where the cancer was. But below the surface, cancer cells had their own goal. It was their mission to spread into the surrounding tissue. Although I couldn't see the unruly cells, I knew they were there, working nonstop against me.

Witnessing the physical destruction that I could see and contemplating the internal destruction that I couldn't see, made me even more terrified. Cancer couldn't be conquered alone. It's too big, too bad, and too ugly. I knew I needed to lead the fight, but I also needed a phalanx behind me.

But *who* should I tell, and *how* should I tell them? As much as I didn't want to trouble anyone, it was important to let my loved ones know what was happening.

When diagnosed, my friend Krista posted about her breast cancer on social media. One post and everyone in her social circle knew. Even friends of friends extended words of encouragement, which I found gracious but simultaneously awkward. I admired Krista's fortitude but knew that approach wasn't for me. In addition, I was connected to many of our photography clients on social media. If they felt uncomfortable asking for quotes and shoots from someone battling cancer, we'd lose work, and I wouldn't be able to afford the medical bills that I knew were coming. So much was on the line.

"You talk a lot," my friend Mae told me back in college, "but it's rare you share anything private. I'm so happy you share stuff with me now."

Sometimes, it takes an outside perspective to realize something insightful about yourself. She was right. I like privacy. Or maybe it had more to do with trust. Invest time in a relationship, listen closely, learn about the person extensively, and then open up. Privacy was my suit of armor, and it was a big deal to take it off.

And then, there was the responsibility that came with telling people my news. If I was going to burden them with something so heavy, I, at least, owed them regular updates. They'd assume the worst if days passed before I responded to their calls or messages. But what if there were days when I was too tired or had too much work to do? What if there were too many doctor appointments on the schedule to keep up? What then? The more people I told, the more commitments I had.

Who should I tell? My closest friends? Am I obligated to tell family because they are family? And what about the people I choose not to tell? What if some people are offended that they didn't make the cancer-telling "A" list?

Although it wasn't my intention to upset anyone, it seemed inevitable if certain people found out much later than everyone else. I knew they would ask why I didn't tell them sooner. It would be difficult to explain my reasoning. And even if I did, would they, *could they,* understand?

When it comes to cancer, even asking for much-needed support is ridiculously complex.

Out of the shower, I got dressed and sat at my desk to compile a list. I wrote in bold, black letters in my journal, THE SECRET SOCIETY. The name felt appropriate.

I will form a society of people I trust to keep my diagnosis a secret. People that deserve to know. People who already know. A team to help pull me through.

There were four existing members:

1. BRUCE (MY HUSBAND)
2. MARY (MY MOTHER)
3. CHRIS (MY SISTER)
4. DAVID (MY FUTURE BROTHER-IN-LAW)

Who else should I add? I needed to determine *who* I should tell, *how* I should tell them, and *when.*

My father deserved to know. After my parents' divorce, my

mother moved west, but my father stayed back in Nebraska, where my sister and I grew up. Delivering the news would require a phone call, forcing me to actually talk about my cancer. Every time I spoke—*or even thought about it*—I cried. And since my dad has a long history of heart problems, I figured it was best to wait. The status of his membership: pending.

Bruce's mother, Betty, was also on the list. She would likely understand my situation since she survived thyroid cancer when Bruce was a young boy. I knew her outlook would be positive, and she could provide insight on how to overcome it. On the flip side, Bruce's brother, Bob, was in the middle of his own cancer battle. *How much more stress can an eighty-five-year-old woman take?* Although incredibly strong, I didn't want to burden her with the diagnosis until I knew my treatment plan, so I added "pending" next to her name.

Next up, Ozzy. He had been our business partner for the past 17 years. He was quick-witted, spent hours staring through a tele-scope at the night sky, could speak—convincingly—in all types of accents, and spent much of his free time browsing old bookstores for scholarly literature that intimidated most people. He would offer a rational perspective which I desperately needed. But I also knew he'd have specific questions about how my diagnosis might affect business. Until I had answers, I decided to hold off. Besides that, I felt it was important to share the news with him in person. So, again, another membership was marked "pending."

Four incredible girlfriends came to mind: Beth, Mae, Lily, and Utaiwan. Not only are they all strong and intelligent, but I knew they would help me navigate the unknown with their unique characteristics and qualities.

Beth was my best friend from high school. Her shock of orangish-red hair makes her appear fiery, but in reality, she's playful, harmonious, and extremely patient. I respect her creative outlook on life, and it often persuades me to see situations differently. Intelligent and beautifully independent, she's an amazing single mother to her son, and over the years, I've seen her conquer the most challenging problems with finesse. I knew she'd provide valuable insight and help find viable solutions.

With her outgoing and vibrant personality, Mae knows how to make me laugh until my side hurts. My best friend from college, our souls are magically intertwined as we often say random things in unison or have similar experiences happen to us simultaneously. Even though she now lives six hours away in a ski town with her husband and two teen boys, our friendship has remained strong. When I need light to fish me out of the darkness, Mae is always the one that shines.

I met Lily in college, too. She's the type of person who inspires others by living her life based on firm beliefs. When she's not doing a beach cleanup or fighting for a ban on plastic waste, she and her husband garden, do yoga and hike the mountains of Marin County. Without a doubt, knowing Lily has made me a better person, and I knew she'd encourage me to fight with fueled passion. Attentive, thoughtful, and caring, I needed her by my side.

Utaiwan moved to California from Thailand when she was a young adult. We worked together at a photo lab in Hollywood after I graduated from college. She's a nurturer at every level, always cooking homemade Thai food for her friends, offering help before you even realize you need it, and looking after every person she cares about. English is her second language, so the first time she told me, "Goodnight, sweet tea," instead of "sweetie," I fell in love with her even more. Over the years, my sister has grown especially close to her, so it didn't surprise me when Chris asked her to be one of her bridesmaids. When you need someone to hold your hand, Utaiwan always steps up to grasp it.

But *how* should I share the news? Unlike an emotional phone call, an email would allow me to carefully set the tone, edit my words, and give me time to think about what I wanted to say.

With my fingers resting on my computer's keyboard, I paused. *What will be my approach? Do I want to come off sad? Scared? Anxious? Strong? Confident? Maybe even overly optimistic? What is my cancer-telling persona?*

I decided to broach the subject with a lighter tone to minimize the worry. I figured a confident, semi-upbeat approach was best.

DEAR FRIEND,

I HAVE SOME DIFFICULT NEWS TO SHARE. A FEW WEEKS AGO, I DISCOVERED A LUMP IN MY RIGHT BREAST. OF COURSE, I PANICKED. AFTER A MAMMOGRAM AND BIOPSY, THE PATHOLOGY REPORT CONFIRMED THAT I HAVE CANCER.

IT WAS ONE OF THE WORST DAYS OF MY LIFE. I'M MOSTLY IN SHOCK, ALTHOUGH IT IS BECOMING MY NEW REALITY. I CHOSE TO EMAIL YOU BECAUSE IF I CALLED, I'D PROBABLY END UP SOBBING, UNABLE TO TELL YOU WHAT NEEDS TO BE SAID. I MUSTN'T PUT ANY ADDED STRESS ON YOU, BUT IT'S SOMETHING FOR YOU TO KNOW.

I AM POWERING THROUGH. ALL I CAN DO IS TAKE THIS SITUATION ONE APPOINTMENT AT A TIME. I'M UNSURE OF WHAT WILL HAPPEN NEXT.

PLEASE DON'T CALL ME TO DISCUSS IT. I THINK ABOUT IT EVEN WHEN I SLEEP. WHENEVER THERE'S A SHORT REPRIEVE, I USE IT TO TRY TO FEEL NORMAL AGAIN.

PLEASE KEEP IT OUR SECRET. TUCK IT AWAY FROM SOCIAL MEDIA OR TELLING OTHERS. I TRUST THAT YOU'LL KEEP THE SECRET SAFE.

I'M STILL EXCITED TO ENTERTAIN OUR FRIENDS, RALPH AND PATRICIA, WHO WILL BE VISITING FROM NEW YORK CITY, EVEN THOUGH I'M UNSURE HOW I WILL JUGGLE ENTERTAINING WITH PROJECTS AND MY ENDLESS NUMBER OF DOCTOR APPOINTMENTS. NONETHELESS, SOMEHOW IT WILL WORK OUT. IT ALWAYS DOES.

SORRY TO PUT YOUR DAY IN A TAILSPIN.

LOVE,

JENNIFER

As I sent off four emails back-to-back, a weight lifted with every click of the 'send' button. There was a sense of freedom in sharing the news with the people closest to me, relief that my secret was out, but to only a select few. I quickly sent out a preemptive text to warn them of what was waiting for them in their inbox.

ME: I SENT YOU AN EMAIL, BUT PLEASE BE HOME WHILE READING.

The upsetting information needed the proper environment to be absorbed. It isn't the type of information that should be processed while dropping a child off at school, preparing for a work presentation, or even ordering breakfast at a café.

While the momentum was still high, it was time to share the news with my mother's side of the family. Creating a direct link between myself and my three aunts, one uncle, and three cousins would ensure accuracy and prevent my mother from being asked the flurry of questions I knew would soon follow.

I composed a group email to the Wells Family, promising to update them regularly. Seven more people were added to THE SECRET SOCIETY with a single click. The tally was up to 15 members. The population of my village had increased significantly.

The responses trickled in throughout the day:

BETH: I WANT TO WRAP YOU UP IN THE BIGGEST HUG.

LILY: I'M HERE FOR YOU.

MAE: I HAD A STRANGE FEELING THAT SOMETHING WAS WRONG, BUT KNOW YOU'LL BE OKAY.

UTAIWAN: I'LL DRIVE YOU TO YOUR APPOINTMENTS IF YOU NEED MY HELP.

AUNT SANDI: SWEET JENN JENN, I KNOW YOU'LL GET THROUGH THIS.

AUNT MARILYN: YOU'RE STRONG LIKE YOUR UNCLE DON.

AUNT CAROLYN AND UNCLE GARY: YOU ARE IN OUR PRAYERS.

COUSIN TAMMY: Since I went through a cancer diagnosis, let me know if I can help.

COUSIN PAM: You're in my daily thoughts.

COUSIN CHAD: I'm sending you a book to read. It's called *Man's Search for Meaning*.

For the time being, THE SECRET SOCIETY was complete.

MEDITATION WITH A PURPOSE

TWO THINGS RELIEVED my anxiety and fear: deep sleep and meditation. I began meditating, often numerous times throughout the day, when I needed a reprieve from the negative thoughts that had taken residence in my brain. And while feeling completely helpless without a treatment plan, I knew it was the only way to proactively self-heal.

Growing up in Nebraska in the 1980s and early '90s, meditation was, for the most part, unconventional. I didn't know a single person who practiced it. There were no churches or Buddhist temples that advocated meditation and no meditation bible. No one had ever suggested I try it until Dr. Scott brought it up at one of my annual physicals long before my diagnosis.

While waiting for my nerves to calm down enough to retake my blood pressure (due to my White Coat Hypertension phobia), Dr. Scott asked, "Have you ever meditated?"

"Medicated?" I asked with a smile.

She grinned at my joke. "If you meditate right, it can feel that way." And then laughed at her own.

"I've never tried it," I said, not wanting to tell her that I perceived people who meditated as strange. I'd always pictured meditators sitting cross-legged on a rock overlooking something scenic. Their palms were open to the sky, resting on their knees, and their fingers curled into an unnatural circular sign that the rest of us would recognize as "okay," but I often questioned whether they were.

"You should," Dr. Scott advised. "You're the type of person whose mind can influence how your physical body reacts. I think you might like it."

If I hadn't adored Dr. Scott as much as I did, I wouldn't have agreed to look into it to validate her suggestion. By the time I left her office, the idea was forgotten. But unknowingly, the seed was still planted.

Two years later, before my diagnosis, the concept of meditation came up again. This time, it wasn't Dr. Scott who suggested it, but Lily, who had just listened to me tell her how stressed I was in my career.

"It's grounding," she said, suggesting I try Deepak Chopra's 21-day online meditation. "If it helped me, it might help you."

"It sounds interesting," I told her, not yet fully committed to the idea.

"It's free," Lily said, which were the exact words I needed to hear. After my first meditation session, I was inspired. And by the twenty-first day, I was hooked.

I told Lily over the phone, "No one has ever told me *not* to think before. It feels amazing to be in the present moment and just exist." My entire life, I thought being busy was better than doing nothing. To achieve things in life, I had to be a doer.

It was such a revelation, that I made meditation part of my daily practice. Eventually, I sat comfortably, cross-legged on the floor, spine straight, with open palms on my knees. Even my fingers were in the "okay" position, which I now know is referred to as *Gyan Mudra*. It felt natural to me, and after some practice, I didn't need a soothing voice to guide me.

At the end of every session, I'd silently ask the Universe:

What is my life purpose?

As much as I enjoyed my photography career, something substantial was missing. There had to be more to life than producing photo shoots or taking pictures that made consumers want to buy more stuff. I longed to give back, create a positive impact, and become a better person.

A year before my diagnosis and every day after it, I asked the same question, hoping to discover an answer. *What is my life purpose?*

And now, after a cancer diagnosis and possibly a shortened lifeline, there was an urgency to find out what it was even sooner. I kept asking the Universe the same question at the conclusion of every meditation, sometimes three or four times a day.

What is my life purpose?

What is my life purpose?

What is my life purpose?

Although I desperately searched for an answer, once the question escaped my lips, it seemed to disappear, as if lost in the vastness of space.

To take my self-healing further, I eventually decided to customize my meditation. I'd lie down, get comfortable, close my eyes, take some deep breaths, and then visualize a radiant healing light in a soothing color. Sometimes, it was turquoise, often bright white, and on occasion, a shade of yellow that warmed my soul like sunshine. The color's brilliant light flowed throughout my body as it enveloped me from the top of my head down to my toes. Gradually, I'd redirect the healing light to the tumor in my right breast as I envisioned the light becoming more vibrant and powerful. It was the only way I knew how to heal my body. The practice was also mentally and emotionally empowering, disconnecting me from all the worry, anxiety, and fear. *(I included the Healing Light Meditation in the back of this book as a reference in case you'd like to try it.)*

No matter which type of meditation I practiced, I'd end the session with the same old question, hoping to achieve some profound wisdom. *What is my life purpose?*

* * *

A message appeared in my inbox from one of THE SECRET SOCIETY members.

BETH: The minute I got your email, I made an appointment for my long overdue mammogram. Your story inspired me.

"Well, at least my cancer did *something* positive," I said quietly to myself after reading the email. *Did I use "cancer" and "positive" in the same sentence?* It seemed absurd that my subconscious had connected the two.

The following morning, I received a text from Lily.

LILY: I just booked a mammogram.

It didn't stop there. A voicemail appeared on my phone during a conference call. When I clicked over to check the message, it was Mae. She said in her usual energetic voice, "You'd be proud! I booked a mammogram! If it can happen to you, it can happen to anyone."

And not long after, my phone pinged:

UTAIWAN: I'm due for a mammogram in the next couple of months. I have already booked my appointment for two months and one day from now.

I was stunned. All four women decided to schedule their mammograms within 24 hours of each other. *Does my crisis have the power to inspire real action?* It couldn't prevent my loved ones from getting cancer, but it could certainly help them catch it early if they did. As I pondered the remarkable concurrence of their decision to get checked, I wondered, *what if my story can influence more women to get checked? Can more lives be saved?* And then I realized that it wasn't a coincidence at all.

It might seem ironic that it took a cancer diagnosis to show me my life purpose, but it did. A life-threatening illness brought me closer to discovering why I was born in the first place.

The booklet that Dr. Myers gave me!

I rushed to the cabinet and searched through the rows of books to find—*What is Breast Cancer?* I needed to learn everything about the disease. If I was going to use my own story to encourage people to prevent it, I needed to know more about cancer itself. *Who gets it, and what causes it?*

As I began flipping through the pages, I realized how ignorant I was. Cancer was growing inside me, yet I didn't know basic facts about the disease.

The information was interesting:

MEN CAN GET BREAST CANCER EVEN THOUGH THE RISK IS LOW.

ONE IN EIGHT WOMEN WILL BE DIAGNOSED WITH BREAST CANCER.

EXCEPT FOR SKIN CANCER, BREAST CANCER IS THE MOST COMMON CANCER IN WOMEN IN THE UNITED STATES.

I drank in the information, committing the facts to memory. When the phone rang, it startled me. The topic of cancer was more engaging than I had initially thought.

"Jennifer?"

"Yes."

"Dr. Fez wanted me to call you to schedule an ultrasound and stereotactic breast biopsy," a nurse said. "My next back-to-back appointments are on May tenth. How does that day work for you?"

I shuffled through a stack of papers on my desk to find the calendar. It was May 8. Although the bruising from my targeted mammogram was fading, the tumor inside of me wasn't.

"That works," I said. Finding a notepad, I scribbled down; ASK

MOM IF SHE IS AVAILABLE ON MAY 10. *I could use her support.*

As soon as I hung up the phone, I flipped the page of the booklet to find a detailed anatomical illustration of a female breast. I perused the diagram pausing on the lobules, bringing the booklet closer, I focused on the ducts. I studied the circular areola the size of a quarter and, finally, the nipple, which was tilted downward like a tiny top hat, as if the breast were taking a bow.

In all the years I've carried around breasts, I had no idea how intricate and essential each part was. Up to this point, I found them to be a nuisance. They caused a button-down shirt to gape, and if I wore a blouse that showed cleavage, I had to be content with random people gawking at them. But now, with their presence threatened, they became beautifully sacred. I was desperate to keep them.

The booklet described cancer cells as "abnormal and uncontrolled." I thought of them as troublemakers, trying to constantly invade and pillage like miniature tyrants. Their goal was to take over, murdering healthy cells that dared to get in their way. Cancer cells don't spread like spilled water on a cloth. They create camps in strategic places allowing them to attack multiple organs at once.

The following heading, "Chemotherapy," made me stop as my heart pumped with fear. I had mustered enough courage to learn about breast cancer, but I couldn't entertain the idea of chemo. Having cancer was bad enough; the idea of undergoing chemotherapy sent me into a cold sweat.

I closed the booklet and took a deep breath. As much as I wanted to have an abundance of knowledge to help others, there was a barrier that I still couldn't cross.

A NIGHT OF NORMALCY

WITH THE THOUGHT of chemotherapy still hovering over me, even though I tried to meditate as often as possible, between sessions, the brokenness crept back in.

It wasn't the first time in my life that I'd felt broken. Broken with heartache. Broken from regret. Broken from total exhaustion. But a cancer diagnosis carried me the furthest away from my usual upbeat self.

Post-diagnosis, all my feelings morphed into one indescribable emotion. I was filled with gratitude yet miserable, grumpy yet happy, and when feeling confident, I felt as if the confidence was a curse. The overload was so intense that the only thing I knew how to do, was cry.

I cried while reading emails. Cried while making dinner. I even cried while watching funny videos online. Somehow, I had become the girl who carried a crumpled, damp tissue in her hand wherever she went, even crying at the depressing thought of crying so much.

At first, Bruce would do his best to comfort me by kissing the top of my head or hugging me. But when it got to the point that I was crying multiple times per day, it was obvious he didn't know what to do, so he changed his tactics.

Instead of asking if I was alright, he said he loved me. When he walked into my office and saw my eyes glazed over with sadness, he'd say, "I love you," before simply carrying on with what he was doing. When he saw me return from the grocery store, still wearing sunglasses with tear-streaked cheeks, he leaned in while unpacking the groceries and said, "I love you." Every night before I fell asleep, he would tuck me in with, "I love you." After hearing the phrase so many times, I started to reciprocate with words instead of keeping my feelings for him inside. After 12 years of marriage, discussing car insurance premiums or our weekly shopping list had replaced the "I love you's," but a cancer diagnosis, as it turns out, can change that.

I'd yell out the screen door when he was outside spraying weeds, "I love you!" When he was reading a history book on the sofa, I'd plant a kiss on his forehead and say, "I love you." Even when the volume was turned up too loud on the television, which previously annoyed me, out came, "I love you."

Our house had become filled with love, partially because it made the misery easier to tolerate but also because having a cancer diagnosis makes you realize how much you love someone.

According to F. Scott Fitzgerald, "We are all drunk on the idea that love, and only love, can heal our brokenness." Drunk on the idea or not, it can undoubtedly mend our brokenness for a little while.

Feeling madly in love, I agreed to go with Bruce for a night out with friends. The New Yorkers, Ralph and Patricia, were in town, staying with Will and Marine, who were artists that had moved to Palm Springs years ago after spending too many harsh winters in

"The Big Apple." The plan was to get together for drinks at Will and Marine's house and then head out for dinner.

But when we pulled into their driveway and parked, I couldn't go in. My bold-colored lipstick couldn't hide the quiver in my lips if my emotions suddenly took over. It wasn't just me and Bruce going to dinner. It was me, Bruce, and my cancer diagnosis. As much as we wanted to keep it hidden, I couldn't trust that the uncontrollable sadness wouldn't pay us a visit at the worst possible time.

As Bruce opened his car door, I stopped him. "It's only been nine days since my diagnosis. I'm not sure how I am going to do this."

He grabbed his wallet from the console and assured me, "It's our secret, and we'll keep it that way." It sounded optimistic but impossible.

"So much has happened since we last saw everyone. How will they *not* know?"

Before Bruce could answer, the front door swung open, and Will enthusiastically waved us inside. I got out of the car as the entire group filtered onto the porch to welcome us with hugs.

"It's been so long," Ralph bellowed in his Brooklyn accent.

"Too long!" Patricia added before he was finished.

In their living room, we sipped merlot and talked about ordinary things: the photo industry, gallery openings, politics, and what Will and Marine should name their new Labrador puppy. Settling on "Jasper" was the most significant achievement of the night. It felt so light, not having the heaviness of a cancer diagnosis weighing down every thought, action, and word.

At the restaurant, we passed around appetizers, sipped martinis, and enjoyed delectable meals that only trained chefs could create. When we dug our forks into a large slice of decadent cheesecake, a miracle happened: I forgot about my cancer. In fact,

I didn't think about it all. My focus was on living life instead of less life to live.

It was a reprieve from reality, a glimpse backward into normalcy. At that moment, we were free from the burden, the secret, the diagnosis. It was something we both so desperately needed.

On our drive home, with the windows rolled down, we shared a sense of freedom as the warm night air whipped through the car, and I felt a sense of relief. "I am so glad we kept it a secret," I confessed to Bruce. I imagined how different the conversation and mood would have been if we hadn't.

"Me too." He looked over, grinned, and placed his hand on my knee. We were just a typical married couple, coming home after socializing with friends. It was something I had taken for granted before.

In bed, he rolled over to say his usual "I love you" before turning out the light on his bedside table.

"I love you, too," I whispered back in the dark.

But that wasn't the only extraordinary thing that happened. For the first time in several nights, I didn't wake up with *Nightly Shockwaves*. I slept peacefully for a solid eight hours. I wasn't exhausted from all the worry; I was exhausted from all the fun.

THE PINK RIBBON OF SOLIDARITY

TEN DAYS AFTER MY DIAGNOSIS, I was back at the women's clinic for an ultrasound on Lefty and a stereotactic breast biopsy on Righty scheduled afterward. As the diagnostic medical sonographer smeared the goopy gel over my armpit and left breast, I laid back and stared up at the ceiling with nothing else to do but listen to the computer fan occasionally kick on to cool itself.

As always, I needed to release some nervous energy, so I blurted out, "I found the lump by accident," hoping that the sonographer might take an interest and we could initiate a conversation. She looked at me curiously, so I continued, "Only nine months ago, I had a clean mammogram."

She moved the transducer wand up and over my breast and, with mild interest, responded, "It's so good that you found it."

"Through all of the craziness, I actually feel fortunate," I remarked, which was honest, but I also hoped to keep the conversation going.

As unlucky as I was to have cancer, I did feel extremely grateful. Grateful that a sneeze caused the pulled muscle and that the tumor in my breast was located where I could actually feel it.

Most importantly, I was grateful to have found the golf ball-sized lump when I did before it grew any larger.

"I know it's important to perform monthly self-checks," she told me, "but honestly, I don't know many women who do. Even women in the healthcare industry don't."

I thought, *why don't more women perform self-breast exams?* Let's be honest, it's easier to get a mammogram where a doctor will determine the status for you. But even if I tried to perform a self-check back in my pre-cancer days, I had no clue what a lump might feel like. Some breast tissue is a bit lumpy anyway. And even though I had just learned that most breast lumps are benign, I knew I'd panic if I ever believed I had felt one (which clearly, I had). As difficult as it is to admit, life is easier when you live in denial. Without feeling a lump, your life stays on track. The moment you feel one, your life instantaneously spins out of control like a car hitting black ice in the middle of a blizzard.

"How is your husband handling all of this?" She was the first person to ask me that question as she documented different areas of Lefty with the wand.

"He's been amazing and so supportive."

"Sometimes it's too much for the family or spouse to handle. Did you hear about the journalist from Mexico who was also diagnosed with breast cancer?"

"Nope."

"When she told her husband, he confessed that he no longer loved her and wanted to file for divorce. He said that the cancer was *her* problem and not to expect any special treatment from him. I hear many women have to seek a counselor for professional advice," she said, "because it's common for spouses and family members to not offer support." But then she raised an eyebrow as if the story was about to take an exciting turn. "You know how people talk about karma?"

"Uh-huh," I said, fully engaged.

"Once the divorce was finalized, and she was cancer-free, *he* got diagnosed with stage four prostate cancer." Picking up the phone receiver and dialing the radiologist's number, she avouched, "Karma's a bitch."

Yes. It. Is.

I only hoped that my karma was good from this point forward. I needed the ultrasound results to confirm that Lefty was cancer-free. If the radiologist discovered additional abnormalities, I knew what would follow: more biopsies, appointments, and mammograms, which would only prolong the start of treatment.

The radiologist entered. He was hunched over and had wild eyebrows that poked out over the rim of his glasses. "I'm Dr. Isaac," he mumbled, immediately turning his back to me to examine the monitor.

Observing him, I was confident he had been reviewing sonograms since Eisenhower. If years of experience count, he was deucedly overqualified.

He cleared his throat and said, "Well...," and then licked his lips. After what felt like an eternity, he finally spoke in a way that reminded me of the Great Oz. "I reviewed the images and have concluded that nothing is abnormal in your left breast."

I heaved a loud sigh of relief. There was finally a sliver of cyan-sky peeking through the tenebrous storm clouds. *Could the worst part be behind me?* I didn't want to get too excited, but maybe I wouldn't have to lose a breast or do chemotherapy. Maybe this could all be fixed with a simple outpatient surgery. And if so, things would get back to normal sooner than later.

As Dr. Isaac hobbled out, the sonographer checked the time. "Let me walk you across the hall for your next appointment," she offered.

As I followed her, I saw my mom sitting in the waiting room reading a magazine. I was grateful that she'd been able to take off work to be with me. Although there was no time to talk, I wanted to let her know how it was going. When she heard the woman say, "Here's the biopsy room," she lifted her head. Before walking inside, I did a quick thumbs-up.

She mouthed the words, "Good luck."

* * *

This biopsy room was a five-star suite compared to Dr. Fez's biopsy room. There were bookshelves, desks, comfortable chairs, and a machine that required a step stool to reach the raised platform. If I had to conjure up the spirit of Grandma Wells for this one, she would have space to meander around and not squeeze past the base of the bed by my feet.

"Take a seat," a nurse told me as two more nurses prepared the room.

As I watched them work, I was reminded of something that a few members of THE SECRET SOCIETY had asked. They wanted to know what 'stage' my cancer was, but I wasn't sure. None of the medical professionals I'd seen so far had mentioned it.

"I'm Dr. Hernandez," the young doctor said with a smile as if she was fulfilling her lifelong dream of working in medicine.

"What stage is my cancer?" I responded, skipping all the greetings and small talk that usually transpire when you first meet someone.

"I'm sorry?" The smile dropped from her face.

"What stage is my cancer?"

She thumbed through my file and then offered, "It appears that the mass is a little less than three centimeters."

Did she not understand my question? Stage I, II, III, or IV? What did the size of the tumor have to do with it?

"Do you think my cancer has spread to my lymph nodes?" I asked, taking a different approach.

"From what we can tell, nothing seems affected. But to be

sure, the surgeon will remove some lymph nodes during surgery. May I tell you about today's biopsy?"

Even medical professionals avoid in-depth conversations about cancer. It's understandable that in situations like mine, there are lots of tests to do before they can determine the best course of treatment, and then there are a lot of decisions to be made beyond that. But it was frustrating. I wanted someone to explain it to me. They were the experts, and I wasn't. They knew cancer, and I didn't.

I nodded, and she continued, "During the stereotactic breast biopsy, we will determine how much tissue within your right breast has cancer cells. You will lie face down on your stomach. There's an opening in the platform for you to place your breast into, which will be compressed. Now it's perfectly normal to experience discomfort during the process. My team will instruct you on how to position your body, and once in place, you must remain perfectly still. They'll take X-rays to determine any breast abnormalities. Once confirmed, I'll return to the room, inject a local anesthetic into your breast, and we'll do more X-rays before I remove samples."

"I'm ready," I told her, eager to get it over with.

A team member held my hand to stabilize me as I climbed the short flight of stairs, the same way you'd help a toddler climb up a slide on a playground.

"Can you scoot your body up an inch?" a different nurse asked. I scooted. "Are you able to twist your body slightly to the left?" I twisted. "Now, turn your head toward the back wall."

Unable to see what they were doing, I relied on my hearing to gauge what was happening in the room. Footsteps rushed around. There were faint conversations that I couldn't make out. The door creaked. I recognized Dr. Hernandez's voice, but it was too soft to make out what she was saying. I had no idea what was going on or why it was taking so long.

Is this normal?

Stretched into position like a fallen department store mannequin, topless, I answered my own question. *No, nothing about this is normal.* I wasn't in pain, but I was uncomfortable, to say the least. It wasn't awkward enough to conjure up the ghost of Grandma, but I still needed a solid distraction.

My peripheral vision caught a poster hanging on the wall of the familiar breast cancer ribbon. I really looked at it ... the curl, center loop, and angled ends.

How can something so delicate represent something so deadly?

Each October, I'd noticed the pink ribbon that cropped up everywhere, from signs at car dealerships to T-shirts to shops where refrigerator magnets are sold. But during the other 11 months, it seemed to disappear from the news, becoming an afterthought until the following year. It felt trendy and seasonal, like the sudden popularity of "pumpkin spice" beverages.

Stretched out on the biopsy table, unsure of what might happen to me, scared of what the biopsy might show, unclear about the stage of my cancer, fearful that it might have spread to my lymph nodes, and sickened by the thought of chemotherapy, something about that ribbon symbol struck me. For the first time, the symbol became meaningful.

A beautiful pink ribbon of solidarity.

I wasn't the first to lie on the biopsy table or experience fear of the unknown. So many women had come before me. Thousands. *Hundreds of thousands.* Regardless of the outcome, they paved the way with their strength and dignity. The pink ribbon represented a sisterhood of women—and men—fighting the same battle.

The more I pondered and listened to the footsteps and hushed voices around me, the more I realized that the ribbon also represents the network of doctors and nurses who show up daily to help us. It represented the scientists working tirelessly to find a cure, as well as every caregiver that has walked beside their loved one going through it. The ribbon did not only stand for patients but for all the others, too.

My thoughts were interrupted by Dr. Hernandez's nearby voice, "You can get down now." I still had no idea what was happening. The same nurse who had helped me up helped me back down as Dr. Hernandez told me she had some good news. "We can't locate any abnormal tissue around the mass. It seems to be contained within the tumor. A biopsy will not be needed today."

I can't wait to tell Mom!

I got dressed and rushed to the waiting room, beaming. My mother was flipping through a design magazine when she looked up, visibly surprised by the broad smile on my face.

"How did it go?" She set the magazine down and followed me into the hallway.

"It didn't," I replied with a new wave of confidence. "They couldn't find any affected tissue outside of the tumor."

Her eyes widened with delight, and her face lit up, "Oh honey, that's amazing. And the ultrasound?"

"There's no cancer in Lefty."

She threw her arms around me. "I'm so happy for you!" A win for me was a win for her. "Your sister's been texting. Let's call her when we get outside to fill her in."

INSTINCTUAL TRUST

THE FOLLOWING DAY, I steeled myself for my walk into the expansive medical center to meet with my surgeon for the first time. I hoped my good luck would continue and my treatment plan wouldn't consist of the other sickening "C" word—Chemotherapy.

Before checking in with the receptionist, I received a text.

BETH: DO YOU THINK YOU'LL HAVE TO DO CHEMO?

ME: I HOPE NOT. GOING TO FIND OUT MY TREATMENT PLAN TODAY.

BETH: HAVE YOU RESEARCHED OPTIONS?

ME: I'LL CALL YOU LATER.

There wasn't time at that moment to elaborate. My reasoning was best discussed over the phone since it was too complicated to explain in a text.

A while back, long before my diagnosis, I was at a friend's cocktail party and met a woman who was battling breast cancer. Curious, I asked, "What's been the hardest part?"

Without hesitation, she said, "Second-guessing my treatment plan. If another woman with breast cancer starts to get well faster or suffers fewer side effects, I start to doubt my own."

It was the only conversation I remembered from that night. I wasn't sure how she had gathered information from other women about their experiences, but I knew now that seeking out that information, whether in person or online, would also leave me confused. Even with a wealth of valuable information available through medical articles and cancer blogs—I figured that, like any ailment, the data would be conflicting. And left to decipher which study or scholarly article to believe would only result in unwarranted doubt. Trying to become an expert overnight wouldn't be as advantageous, at least for me, as listening to the professionals who had spent years studying medicine, specializing in oncology, and are up to date with the latest clinical trials and research. It was my job to be the patient; their job to be the doctor. So, I opted to trust the process and, most of all, my instincts. If the doctor seemed untrustworthy and my gut told me something was off, I'd seek a second opinion. If not, I'd listen to their advice, be open, trust the process, and move forward.

So, no, as peculiar as it may seem, I hadn't researched options.

I'd barely arrived at the waiting room when an austere nurse with a thick German accent called out my name. Tall, with permanent frown lines etched around her mouth, she wore her scrubs with authority. I quickly raised my hand to identify myself among the mass of people and followed her back to an examination room.

"Sit down," she stated. "I'm Katja, Dr. Hu's nurse."

Her name brought back memories of a Katja I knew in college. She was from Germany, too, and made homemade schnitzel and shortbread cookies and was always generously sharing them with her classmates. But this Katja wasn't warm and sweet like that one.

"Are you taking any medicines?" By the tone of her voice, I could tell she was irritated.

"No."

"Are you experiencing any pain or discomfort?"

"Right now?"

"Of course, right now," she chirped back.

"No."

I was pretty sure she didn't want me to bring up the incredibly uncomfortable conversation transpiring between us. I wanted to verbalize how crummy my life had become and how there was never a better time to show compassion. But instead, I remained quiet as her fingers pounded the keyboard like rain striking a tin roof.

Based on her lousy attitude and tough demeanor, it was easy to make an assumption that she hated her job. I mean, *hated* it. But I had to step back and remind myself that this woman was here to assist me. So, the only rational thing to do was to shift my perspective, give her a chance, and show some respect, even if it wasn't reciprocated. After all, she's on my side, TEAM JENNIFER, even if she wished to be someplace else.

Instead of feeling intimidated, I did the opposite. I decided to talk. "I found the lump myself and was diagnosed with cancer eleven days ago. It's a lot for me to handle."

Her fingers stopped typing, and she said, "You take good care of yourself. It just shows that cancer can happen to anyone." *Was that a compliment?* "If I were you right now, my blood pressure would be off the charts." *Wait, was that some empathy behind the disgruntled demeanor?*

"Trust me; I'm super stressed," I admitted.

She sat upright in her chair, now distracted from gathering information for Dr. Hu. "I wouldn't be able to work right now. My only focus would be having the surgeon remove cancer as quickly as possible."

"I am hoping for a surgery date soon," I shared.

She stared at me briefly before asking, "What's it like to have cancer without a treatment plan?"

I couldn't believe it. It was a great question, and yet, how could I sum up the fears and emotions in a way that would make sense to someone who has never been diagnosed? How do I explain everything that comes with a diagnosis, from deciding *who* to tell and *how* I should tell them? Do I detail the sleepless nights? How do I convey that the scenery is flying past faster than I can recognize, and yet it feels as if the train is barely moving and I may never reach my destination?

But through all of that, I heard myself answer with, "I guess it's like being in a boxing ring, gearing up to fight an opponent when every light in the gym goes black. Unsure of which direction they're going to appear, I swing and punch nothing but air. I keep swinging and swinging, but there's nothing to hit. Exhausted, I want to stop, but I can't afford to stop swinging. The real fight hasn't even begun. Even though I am completely depleted without an ounce of energy left, I must continue to protect myself, or else I'll be attacked and possibly killed."

Her mouth fell open. Even I was shocked by the profundity of my response. *Where did that come from?*

"Let me go get Dr. Hu," she said. "I'll come back to finish up after you two have talked." She handed me a folded medical gown and left.

There was just enough time between changing and meeting Dr. Hu to make a couple of crucial pleas. *Please help me get through all of this. Please let me fix this situation without chemotherapy.*

I heard a soft knock. The doorknob turned, and in walked Dr. Hu. The first thing I noticed was her gentle energy, which had a calming effect on my nerves.

"How are you dealing with your breast cancer diagnosis?" she asked. This was a first. Most doctors talked about the physical aspects, not my emotional well-being.

"Honestly, it's been rough."

"The news is still very raw. You were recently diagnosed." It felt good for someone in the medical profession who deals with cancer regularly to acknowledge what I was going through.

"I'm ready to take the next steps to get rid of it," I said, hinting that she should use her powers to cure me—*without chemotherapy.*

"That's wonderful. First, let's talk about your type of breast cancer, and then we'll discuss treatment options."

My type of breast cancer? Until that moment, I'd assumed all breast cancer was the same, that all cancer was the same, differentiated only by the organ it chose to initially attack.

But first, THE SECRET SOCIETY still needed an answer, so I asked on their behalf, "What stage of cancer do I have?"

"Well, we know it's not stage zero because it has moved outside the ducts." *I thought staging only went from one to four.* "The size of the mass determines staging, too. But also, it's important to know if any cancer has had access to blood vessels and lymph nodes. I will remove some lymph nodes during surgery to have them tested. As a doctor, it's important not to guess." She paused and then asked, "Does that make sense?"

"Yes." Although I still wanted to know, I was glad she took the time to finally explain why it was impossible to give an accurate answer. It made perfect sense that she simply needed more information.

"There are three main receptors associated with breast cancer," she continued using her fingers to count them down. "They are estrogen, progesterone, and HER2. Your results came back positive for all three. Most cancers are not triple-positive, so it's a bit unusual statistically. Only approximately ten percent of the cases fall into the same category as yours." My initial reaction was that 'triple-positive' sounded bad, *very* bad, *three times* as bad as 'normal' cancer, and my heart fluttered. Before I could ask if my assumption was correct, she continued, "The receptors are fed by estrogen and progesterone hormones. But also, HER2 is another type of receptor that takes signals from outside the cells, causing them to misbehave. This results in the cancer being more aggressive."

I was right! Having triple-positive cancer is definitely worse! Hearing the word "cancer" and "aggressive" in the same sentence was terrifying. Given that I'd had a clear mammogram only nine months before, and now a golf ball-sized lump was growing inside my breast, I'd already sensed it was aggressive.

"How does triple-positive cancer affect my treatment plan?" I asked, hoping for the best possible outcome. *Please do not say the word chemotherapy.*

"With your situation, you're a great candidate for a partial mastectomy, otherwise known as a lumpectomy. It's a breast-conserving surgery, meaning we'd only remove the cancerous tumor and a buffer zone of tissue around it. In other words, you'll be able to keep your breast. *Great news!* "But to do a lumpectomy, we will need to shrink the tumor in size with chemotherapy, followed by radiation post-surgery."

She just said the other "C" word.

My heart thumped furiously inside my chest, and my mind frantically searched for alternative options. *If I do a total mastectomy, will I still have to do chemo?* But I didn't want to remove my entire breast either. *Is it better to do chemotherapy or lose a body part?* It all seemed brutally unfair to make such a life-altering decision. *Are there any other choices? Can't we just do a lumpectomy and move on?*

Thrown into a state of panic, my entire nervous system collapsed. The room undulated around me like I was on a merry-go-round. I took deep breaths to prevent vomiting. I watched Dr. Hu's lips form words, but I could no longer understand her. *Don't pass out,* I told myself. Fixated on the idea of chemotherapy, the word repeatedly replayed in my mind. *Chemotherapy! Chemotherapy!* No other thoughts were allowed in. *I can't believe I have to do chemotherapy!* It took every bit of energy to appear normal, and even then, I wasn't sure if I was.

Still lost in my chaotic thoughts, I heard her say, "Of course, if you feel more comfortable having a full mastectomy, we can go that route. How do you feel about your options?" And then, suddenly, there was clarity.

Scanning the room, my eyes landed on a framed photo behind her on the countertop. It was a picture of Dr. Hu with a young girl, building a sandcastle on the beach in matching bathing suits and sun hats. Their smiles were identical.

Trust. My. Instincts.

Steering my gaze from the picture and over to Dr. Hu, I asked, "If I were your daughter in the same situation, would you suggest the same treatment plan for her? Would you put her through chemotherapy?"

Dr. Hu gathered her thoughts while staring up at the ceiling. She then looked at me and firmly said, "Yes. I'd tell her to do the same thing." And I knew she was telling the truth.

As much as I didn't want to do chemotherapy, I trusted her. It was the right path, and we both knew it.

"Okay, let's move forward with the recommended treatment plan," I confirmed. *I am about to become a full-blown cancer patient, unable to hide my secret.*

Before leaving the exam room, Dr. Hu told me that Katja would set me up with an oncologist and that someone would call me from an imaging center in Beverly Hills to schedule a breast MRI. She wanted me to meet with a genetic counselor, too. The appointment list kept getting longer and longer, which meant less time for work or a life outside of illness. Being a cancer patient began to feel like a full-time job.

After I got dressed, the door opened. It was Katja. "Come with me," she said.

Walking through the waiting room, I followed her to the

counter, where she watched the receptionist finish a phone call. I stopped a few steps behind her, letting Katja take the lead.

As soon as the call was finished, Katja asserted, "We need to set her up with an oncologist."

The receptionist clicked on a different computer screen, and I could see the extensive database of names reflected in her reading glasses as she scrolled through them. "What about Dr. Carter?"

"Who else?" Katja asked.

"Dr. Mahoney?"

"Who else?"

The second time Katja rejected a doctor, it dawned on me that she was taking me under her wing and using her personal experience to vet oncologists. My story meant something to her, and she felt like my protector.

"I think I can squeeze her in with Dr. Santos," the receptionist said, hoping the search was over.

"Yes!" She spun around to tell me, "You'll love Dr. Santos. Not only is he the best, but he's from Brazil. Can you meet with a cancer care coordinator for a quick orientation?"

I nodded. Anything to cross an appointment off of what felt like a never-ending "to-do" list. She led me down a hallway, around the corner, and passed me off to a woman who flashed an overzealous, gummy smile.

Why is she so happy? I thought.

NOT A "HOLLYWOOD" THING

"I AM JESSICA, your cancer care coordinator!" A tiny woman announced as if she had just hit a triple espresso high.

When she opened the door to her modest office, it was just that, a nondescript room with a simple wooden desk, a bench on which she told me to sit, metal filing cabinets, and floor-to-ceiling bookshelves crammed full of literature about cancer.

More valuable information to live out my life purpose, I thought. *This is good.*

She pulled a generic canvas tote from her desk drawer. "Let me see," she said as she shimmied a pamphlet off one of the shelves. "This is a fun handout!" *Fun?* I couldn't help but question her choice of adjectives. Crouching down, she pulled a book from the bottom shelf and exuberantly slid it into the bag. "There are so many good cancer resources!"

Am I at a cancer care orientation or a pep rally?

"Oh, oh, oh…" she saw something on the top shelf. On her tiptoes, she stretched her arm out and wiggled her fingertips, pulling a softcover book down. "This is a cookbook for cancer patients. Be sure to make the squash bisque soup. You don't have to have cancer to enjoy that one!"

Dear God. Did she really just say that?

"See this blue paper?" She held it up in front of her chest like a preschool teacher might hold up a picture book for all her students to see. "It's a calendar with free exercise classes you can take. There's yoga, water aerobics, and even belly dancing. And here's a handout to schedule a free makeover. Who doesn't like to have their makeup done professionally?" Down into the bag they all went. "Here's some great information on how to cope during chemotherapy." Another booklet dropped into the bag. She acted as if I were an attendee at some "you got diagnosed with cancer" convention with free giveaways at every booth.

Did she really think I'd be excited to try a new recipe for squash soup or take belly dancing classes?

She moved to the filing cabinets, opened a drawer, and rummaged through them. At this point, I wanted to make up an excuse to leave. But leaving would only require me to come back and finish on another day. I had to stick it out.

"Here it is!" Out swung a mastectomy bra with the strap twisted around her index finger. With a prosthetic silicone gel breast in her other hand, she showed me how to position it neatly into the pouch of the cup. "Women like these bras because they can hug people, and the person can't tell they are missing a breast or two," she boasted.

What the...? This woman was *not* on my side. She was making the experience of having cancer worse. Thirty minutes ago, I was scrambling for a breath when I heard Dr. Hu say, "Chemo-therapy." Now, I was forced to deal with her uber-enthusiastic rambling. Did she think her over-the-top Panglossian demeanor would somehow convince me that having cancer isn't so bad?

"Are you interested in joining a support group?" I wondered if she ever stopped smiling.

"I'm not sure," I muttered. "I don't think so."

"Don't worry, you can decide later," and then she added another sheet of paper to the collection.

Finally, she removed the bag from her shoulder, placing it at my feet like a gift. She pulled out one last book, the finale.

With her arm extended out, she exclaimed, "Here's a catalog for wigs," and waited for me to take it.

I slowly lowered my gaze to the cover. The healthy-looking model wore a fake smile and a short curly blonde wig that in no way resembled natural hair. Completely unable to assess my reaction, the coordinator stared at me, giddy. I couldn't bring myself to accept it or see the pictures inside.

She jiggled her hand. "Take it. It's for you."

I reached out and reluctantly accepted the catalog. When she released her grip, it became mine. I quickly tossed it into the bag, hoping it would somehow disappear into an abyss.

But then, the already disastrous situation took an even sharper turn. "You *do* know your hair is going to fall out, right?" she said, in the same way a more astute person might ask if you are aware that it's forecasted to rain. "But don't worry; they make such cute wigs now." *Stop talking. Please, I beg you, stop talking.* "For some reason, it bothers women to lose their hair. It must be a 'Hollywood' thing."

I was appalled. I was beyond appalled. Even now, I can't find words to convey how mortified I was. *Who in their right mind would let this woman work with cancer patients?* Her bounty of positivity aside, she needed to be educated about what hair loss meant. It wasn't about vanity or an obsession with "Hollywood" at all. It was about exposing my secret and all the personal and professional implications after that. But I knew there was no way to tell her without breaking down.

"I think that covers everything," she informed me, "but feel free to email me with any questions that might come up." *You will never hear from me again,* I thought as I grabbed the stupid canvas bag off the floor and jumped up to leave. Before I could slip out, she said one last thing, "Remember to try the squash bisque soup. I'd love to hear what you think."

* * *

My car tires squealed around the corners of the parking garage as I left. The news about chemotherapy was too heavy to carry alone. I had to tell someone. My mom was at work. Bruce was entertaining Ralph and Patricia, so I dialed my sister's number. She didn't pick up. Against my best judgment, I called Bruce anyway.

Thank God, he answered.

"How's it going?" he asked.

"Where are you?!" I shouted over the noise of a rumbling motorcycle on the freeway.

"We are having lunch on El Paseo. I stepped out of the restaurant when you called. Tell me, how did it go?"

And then—like some trapped animal—I yelled, "I have to do chemotherapy! This is bad! I don't know what to do or how to get through it. This is fucking bad!"

When I paused for a response, all I could hear was Bruce crying on the other end. Under any other circumstance, hearing him cry would have stopped me cold. It would make me realize that screaming at him was not the right way to handle the situation. On any other day, hearing his sniffles and choked sobs would make me feel compelled to comfort him. But not this time. I was in too deep, and I couldn't see past my own pain. At that moment, no one else's pain could compare to mine.

"I'm coming for you," he announced, trying to catch his breath. "I think I should be there with you."

"Don't!" I said, focused exclusively on self-preservation.

"I think I should."

"I am headed to my sister's house. Stay there with Ralph and Patricia. I won't be home tonight and need time to process all of this." I knew the New Yorkers would be staying in our guest room for a couple more nights.

"I want to comfort you and—"

"I'll see you guys tomorrow," I interrupted.

He hesitantly replied, "Okay, but..." and was cut off by my sister beeping in on the other line.

"I have to go." I hung up and switched over to connect with Chris.

"I was on a conference call but just got off. Are you okay?"

"I'll see you in ten minutes," I told her.

"Okay. Drive safe." She knew by the sound of my voice that I wasn't.

I parked the car in front of her house and rushed down the pathway with the canvas bag in hand. She stood there waiting for me with the front door open, a confused look on her face.

"I have to do chemo!" I cried out as I bolted inside to bawl on her sofa.

Chris followed me in and, without saying anything, picked up the canvas bag I'd thrown onto the coffee table. She carefully went through the materials forced upon me as I cried. When opening the wig catalog, she was brave enough to flip through the pages. She familiarized herself with the information, and that was enough.

When finished, she asked, "Do you think you should get a second opinion?"

"No. I like and trust Dr. Hu," I replied.

That night in her guest room, it was impossible to sleep. I had hoped my cancer would require a quick fix, maybe a simple surgery, and life as I knew it would resume. But now, with Dr. Hu suggesting chemotherapy, all hope was lost.

No matter what, I have to keep swinging.

EMBRACE THE JOURNEY

AFTER MY HYSTERICAL call with Bruce, Ralph and Patricia automatically became two new members of THE SECRET SOCIETY. When they found out the news, they packed their bags and left the following morning to give us our space. I missed not being able to spend time with them but appreciated the much-needed solitude.

It was time to stay busy—again—by running errands together. *Lots* of errands. As Bruce drove down the road that hugged the base of the San Jacinto Mountain range, I saw a wooden sign with mustard-colored lettering that read, "Cancer Survivors Park." In all the times we had passed by the park, I had never noticed its name.

"Slow down," I said, intrigued.

The park was small but beautifully landscaped with fuchsia and yellow flowers, and the sidewalk was lined with manicured bushes and blossoming cacti. Bronze sculptures of a boy, an older gentleman, and a middle-aged woman were frozen as they passed through a series of bronze arches. I didn't know it at the time, but the arches represent the cancer journey, and the statues, with determined looks chiseled on their faces, push forward, eager to be cancer-free on the other side.

"When you get well," Bruce told me, noticing the park's name for the first time, too, "we'll go there and take your picture."

It was a sweet gesture. "Yes," I told him, "that sounds great."

"If you don't get well...," but he stopped before finishing the sentence. Stunned that he had let the words slip out, he immediately backpedaled. "I am so sorry. I can't believe I said that." He panicked, frustrated, checking for my reaction as he quickly took his eyes off the road.

But I wasn't upset. Bruce had carried his secret for 12 long days between Dr. Fez's dreadful call and his forced admission to the New Yorkers. The entire time, he had worried about what *might* happen. And yet, he'd tried to be strong for me by not saying what was inevitably on his mind.

During my ultrasound, I remembered the sonographer's question, "How is your husband handling all of this?" The cancer had changed my life and his, and this was the first time I could step outside myself to see it. After my hysteria the day before, it actually felt good to be compassionate and empathetic again.

"I didn't mean that. I am so sorry. Why did I say that?" Bruce kept apologizing.

I patted his shoulder and told him, "I'm not upset." He looked at me, still confused with himself and even more confused by my calm reaction. "I'm not," I said.

I created THE SECRET SOCIETY to contain the news. But at the same time, it isolated Bruce and prevented him from building his own support system. He needed to tell people what he was going through.

"If you need to confide in any of your family or friends about my situation, you can. I trust you and am happy you could share the news with Ralph and Patricia since you are so close with them."

He looked perplexed. "But you wanted me to keep it a secret."

"For the most part, I still do. But it would help if you had people to talk to. Do what's best. I trust your judgment."

"I can't believe I said that," he uttered, still contrite. "I am so sorry."

As we ran our stay-busy errands, depositing a check at the bank and picking up clothes at the cleaners, the busyness didn't stop my mind from collecting more questions. *How many rounds of chemotherapy will I have to do? When will I start? What can I expect in terms of side effects?*

*   *   *

When I got back to the house, I called up the hair expert of the family, Chris. She had styled my hair for both of my high school proms and always knew all the tips and tricks. Although I usually asked my sister, "What should I do *with* my hair?" this time, I asked, "What should I do *without* it?"

"Well, your hair is always pulled back in a ponytail," she explained. "Purchase a ball cap with a fake ponytail attached, and I bet no one will know the difference. Just make sure it's the same blonde color and the correct length." I figured she must have seen one available in the wig catalog she browsed through while I was bawling on her sofa.

I took note but decided to leave the wig-hunting for a different day. Not only was the thought still overwhelming, but I was hopeful that my hair would miraculously remain attached to my head during treatment, even though the effervescent cancer care coordinator thought otherwise.

Besides that, there were more important things pending. Three people remained on the 'I still need to tell them I have cancer' list: my father, my mother-in-law, and our business partner. Even though I didn't have a scheduled treatment plan in place, I decided to add two more names to THE SECRET SOCIETY since I felt emotionally sound that afternoon.

I called my father in Nebraska. Even though I was still apprehensive because of his medical issues, he deserved to know about mine.

He answered his cell phone, slightly out of breath. "How's my beautiful daughter?"

"Good," I lied. It was important to gauge his current health situation first. "How are you feeling?"

"Not as good as Bruce since he's with you today."

My dad, a lifelong salesman, always knew what to say to make whomever he was talking with want to stay and talk some more. He was good at giving compliments and making people laugh.

"Dad, I need to tell you something."

"Okay."

"I have some bad news." *Why is it still so difficult to tell people?* With a deep breath, I forced myself to say, "I found a lump in my right breast, and after a biopsy, I was diagnosed with cancer." There was only silence on the other end. "I have a great medical team and treatment plan with chemo, surgery, and radiation." Still no response. *Did he drop dead of a heart attack?*

Then, he said, "You'll get through this because you're my Jennifer." My father is an optimist, but the fact that he had so much faith in me to overcome cancer felt as if he was glossing over the seriousness of what I had just told him. I wondered if he fully understood the magnitude. His next question suggested he didn't. "So, what do you have planned for the rest of the day?"

That's it? No cancer-related questions? Are we already onto another topic? His unusual reaction threw me off.

"Oh, I'll get some housework done," I muttered. And then reciprocated with, "What about you?"

"Going to water the grass and then grill some ribeye steaks.

You know what makes a great marinade?" *The recipe for a marinade is more critical than discussing my life-threatening illness.*

I was instantly offended. But as he rattled off what seemed like a ridiculously complicated list of ingredients, finally concluding with why parsley flakes work but dried basil is better, I was no longer annoyed. His lighthearted response was precisely what I needed to keep me calm and emotionally steady. Maybe he could sense that, or maybe he was in denial, or perhaps he did care more about the taste of a ribeye than going into detail about some depressing disease. Marinades keep it light. Cancer talk doesn't.

After the subject had moved from marinades to the best way to clean dirty car headlights, I felt hopeful. All this mundane chit-chat somehow made me feel a bit more normal. Besides, it was unlikely he'd go into cardiac arrest if he opted to focus only on grass, grilled meat, and car maintenance.

Let's hope Betty handles the news just as well.

Instead of being out of breath like my father, Bruce's mother answered the phone with the roar of the vacuum cleaner in the background. "Hello," she said, followed by some rustling, and the noise stopped.

"It's me." I knew she'd recognize my voice. "I have to tell you something."

Being a cancer survivor herself, I was interested in her perspective. Diagnosed with thyroid cancer when Bruce was a small boy, Betty's insight would be beneficial.

When I said, "I have breast cancer," she didn't roll past it like my father.

"Oh no," she replied, and then there was a long pause which I decided not to interrupt. "Will you have to do chemo?"

She had been treated with a liquid form of radioactive iodine several decades ago, a standard treatment back then for thyroid cancer. Betty had been able to avoid chemotherapy herself, and her son, Bob, had been given the option of chemo for his colon cancer and refused.

"Yes," I answered. "But I want your advice since you're a survivor. Any tips?"

"Remain busy. Drink plenty of water. Don't stress because it only makes matters worse," she said as if the information was still fresh in her mind.

"I think managing the stress might be the most difficult part."

"Any idea of when you'll have to start chemo?"

"Not yet. I'll keep you updated."

When I hung up the phone, I felt empowered. With only our business partner, Ozzy, remaining, I decided to share the news with him face-to-face before our next photo shoot. It was also time to send out an update to the Wells Family. I sat down at my desk to compose an email.

DEAR FAMILY,

I MET WITH MY SURGEON. HER ADVICE WAS FOR ME TO DO CHEMO-THERAPY TO SHRINK THE TUMOR AND HAVE A LUMPECTOMY SURGERY WHICH WILL ALLOW ME TO KEEP MY BREAST. I'M MEETING WITH MY ONCOLOGIST ON MAY 22. SHE ALSO WANTED ME TO SEE A GENETIC COUN-SELOR AND GET A BREAST MRI FOR MORE IN-DEPTH DOCUMENTATION. I'M OKAY AND TAKING IT ONE DAY AT A TIME. AS SOON AS I KNOW MORE, I'LL CIRCLE BACK.

LOVE,

JENNIFER

Before clicking 'send,' I copied my mom and sister to update them on what was being said. Anxious to inform my sister that I had finally told our dad about the diagnosis and to share his reaction, I picked up the phone to let her know how it went.

But when she answered, her voice was faint and sounded off. *Has she been crying?*

"What's wrong?" I asked.

"I just read your email," she explained, "and my wedding now seems trite."

My heart sank with sadness. It killed me that she felt that way. She had waited her entire life to be engaged to someone like David. She wanted marriage more than anything, and I wanted her to have that.

After his proposal at Disneyland, plans followed for their destination wedding. They decided to get married at a private villa, and as her Matron of Honor and a proud sister, I was excited to be involved. Everyone in the family was thrilled. But since my diagnosis, the questions shifted from wedding dress styles to cancer staging.

How can I make things better for her? How can I make this right?

But then, like some literary scholar, a Friedrich Nietzsche quote came to mind. I had read it back in high school, and I didn't know that I had the ability to recall it until that moment. *"He who has a why to live can bear almost any how,"* I thought. Her wedding was the *why*, and the treatment plan was the *how*. To make it to her wedding, I'd endure anything.

The quote brought me a wave of reassurance. "Your wedding is eleven months away. This will all pass. Life doesn't stop when you're sick, tired, or diagnosed with cancer. Weddings don't either. Your wedding in Jamaica will be perfect, I promise."

She rebutted, "How can you know for sure?"

"It will be."

In all honesty, when it comes to cancer, anything can happen. Chemo treatments are often postponed for various reasons; desired results may or may not occur, and plans change. There was no way to know if the chemo would shrink the tumor in time. No way to tell whether I'd be ready to walk down the aisle before her on May 5, but I carried the hope that I would.

* * *

When the world feels too heavy, I like to go outside and look at the mountains. The magnitude somehow makes my issues—and me—feel small, placing my most significant problems in perspective. When the wind rustles, the cicadas buzz in unison, and I stare into the vast sky; it fills me with gratitude. I love life. I love the world in which I live. All these things, big or small, make up something substantial and worthy.

I sat on my patio watching the wispy clouds until the sky turned a soft shade of magenta and the sun dropped below the horizon. Over those hours, my mind let go of the day, which provided space for an unexpected message to be heard.

The message was:

Embrace the journey. Embrace all of it, even the good and bad. You may not have chosen this journey, but it is, and forever will be, yours.

I sat in silence a little longer, taking in the revelation.

It's true. I didn't choose cancer; cancer chose me. As much as I was desperate to skip past the chemo, surgery, radiation, and everything else that comes with a diagnosis, I needed to experience the lessons that would unfold along the way. I had to embrace it all to become a better version of myself. It was time to "embrace the journey" instead of resisting it.

I didn't know if I could, but I'd try.

BATTERED CONVERSE

I ASKED my cousin Tammy over the phone, "How did you handle losing all of your hair during chemo?" It was the one potential side effect that worried me the most.

"It was difficult. I suggest you purchase the wig before you start treatment so you can be prepared when it happens," she told me.

When it came to survivors, I had a new admiration for them. I was in junior high, idolizing the seniors that I so desperately wanted to become. They learned skills I needed to know. And even though Tammy's cancer was in her lung instead of her breast, the fact that she had managed to become cancer-free gave me confidence in my own journey.

"Is it strange to wear a wig?" I asked.

"When it came down to it, I preferred wearing headscarves." *So it is strange.* "But my sister-in-law, also diagnosed with breast cancer, had a custom wig made and wore hers all the time. She looked beautiful in it."

I knew Betty would let me borrow her wig, but the hair was short and dark brown, vastly different than my own. At a time when my life was in upheaval, the last thing I wanted was a drastic hairstyle change that would surely blow my secret wide open. I longed for normalcy.

I recalled what Chris said, "Purchase a ball cap with a fake ponytail attached, and I bet no one will know the difference."

Taking everything into consideration, I decided to wig-hunt online. I clicked a few search filter boxes: dishwater blonde color, shoulder-length, straight, with a maximum price of three hundred dollars. I quickly realized that wigs made of real human hair are expensive. Too pricey for my budget. Synthetic ones ranged from looking like something you'd wear at Halloween to those that looked pretty convincingly like human hair if you never had the urge to touch it. I was disappointed that, once again in life, money made the difference between feeling like a clown and a human being.

The first photo I clicked on matched the criteria but looked artificial. Scrapping that idea, I checked out ball caps with pony-tails attached, but they had an ersatz quality that was off-putting. There was pressure to choose something, *anything,* even if I didn't like it. I finally settled on a full wig that matched the criteria just shy of my price point.

At least it's something. If Dr. Santos says it's unnecessary, I'll return it for a refund. I was still counting on Dr. Santos—the Brazilian oncologist gifted to me by Katja the German nurse—to assure me that while most people lose their hair during chemo, I would be an exception.

I didn't want to tell Bruce about my recent purchase. I had to like it first. I hated to keep things from him, but this particular thing felt too personal—*too embarrassing*—to discuss at that moment.

As I reached out to several members of THE SECRET SOCIETY to inform them about my progress, I noticed new concerns. It was apparent some of them had been doing their own online research and forming opinions about my diagnosis and treatment plan.

"Why haven't you started chemo yet? Isn't your cancer spreading?"

"Avoid chemotherapy; it's toxic. Have you considered immunotherapy?"

Their intentions were good. I knew they wanted to help but didn't know how, so they were self-educating in an attempt to be my advocate. But being emotionally unstable, mentally confused, and lacking the energy to defend my decisions, I felt defeated.

Maybe I don't have an answer when it comes to which stage my cancer is, but I know its severity. I know what is on the line if I make the wrong decision.

Even though I tried to compartmentalize their opinions, I cared about these people, and these people cared about me. And the fact that their perspectives were so varied added even more pressure, stirring up a new kind of uncertainty. I was trusting my gut, and yet, my mind started to question every decision I had made up to that point.

When I called my mother to tell her about how I was feeling, she shared some words her father told her. "Don't judge a person until you've walked three days in his shoes," she recited. Then she added something of her own, "This is not the time to please others. Trust yourself."

Her advice made me lift my chin and regain my confidence. It also reminded me of a conversation I had with my friend Krista when she was fighting breast cancer.

Krista sat in our studio, confessing the difficulties of her own journey. "I knew in my heart that chemo and radiation weren't right for me," she expressed. "Some people cannot understand why I would refuse conventional treatment and go the holistic route. But I shouldn't have to justify my case to others; I must trust my gut."

At the time, in my pre-cancer way of thinking, I couldn't fathom going against a doctor's advice and deciding on an alternative treatment plan. I had my own opinions about Krista's choices. *Doesn't she know how serious having cancer is?*

Trying to understand, I asked, "How does your mom feel about that decision?" They were close, and if her decision made me uncomfortable, I knew her mother had to feel even worse.

"She gave me a million reasons *why* I should do chemotherapy. She'd bombard me with research, and it was exhausting. At first, I was annoyed, and then I became angry. But it hit me one day after we got into a yelling match."

"What's that?" I asked.

"She was only trying to save me from her own fear of losing me."

Her response made more sense now than it did then. I understood that THE SECRET SOCIETY wanted to keep me in their lives longer, which was a brilliant compliment that made me feel even more loved.

As much as it would have been easier on me if they could've related to my situation—and agreed as a whole—I was glad they stood on the sidelines. They would have to walk three days in my crummy, beaten-down, battered Converse to comprehend the internal turmoil and difficult decisions I faced. I would never want them to have to experience it firsthand. Out of my love for them, I'd listen. But out of self-love, I had to trust my instincts and carry on.

LAUGHTER IS THE BEST MEDICINE

In the 22 days since my diagnosis, I still didn't have any dimpling of my breast, redness, or discharge from my nipple. From time to time, I'd feel a sudden pinch in Righty, which caused my anxiety to soar, worried that cancer was consuming more of my healthy cells and growing bigger by the day.

When I walked into the exam room for my appointment with Dr. Santos, I realized why Katja adored him. By the number of accolades that hung on the wall, housed in gold shiny frames, it was obvious he had an excellent track record as an oncologist. Dressed in my usual medical gown—which felt like my new uniform for the full-time position I had acquired as a patient—I was anxious to meet this successful and award-winning doctor in person. And when he finally entered the room *(okay, I'll state another obvious),* he was handsome and could have easily played a doctor on a soap opera with his short, sleek, blackish-brown hair, dark eyes, and tanned skin.

"Nice to meet you," he said in his Brazilian accent. Despite being confident and charismatic, he quickly got to the point, which I appreciated. "Your breast cancer is triple positive, which is ER positive, PR positive, and HER2 positive. It doesn't sound good, but there is a lot of research on treating each component. You're sitting in a much better place today than someone with the exact diagnosis two years ago."

"Do you think I may have cancer in my lymph nodes?" The pinching in my breast prompted me to ask that important question again, even though Dr. Hu had explained why it was impossible to give an accurate answer.

"There are tests we can do to find out, but the most important thing right now is to shut cancer down. I am going to shut cancer down," he said, with a level of conviction I hadn't heard from a doctor before.

He pulled a folded piece of paper from the pocket of his lab coat and handed it to me. It was a list.

- SIX ROUNDS OF CHEMOTHERAPY, THREE WEEKS APART
- 12 MONOCLONAL ANTIBODY THERAPY INFUSIONS, WITHOUT CHEMOTHERAPY, THREE WEEKS APART
- LUMPECTOMY SURGERY
- RADIATION, 4-5 WEEKS
- PRESCRIPTION MEDICINE, A TAMOXIFEN PILL, TAKEN EVERY DAY FOR FIVE YEARS

To him, it was a roadmap for success. For me, the list was long and crippling. I had to focus on the first step: chemotherapy. *I'll take the rest as they come,* I thought.

"Do you have children?" Dr. Santos asked.

"No."

"Do you want to have kids?"

"No," I affirmed, glad Bruce and I had discussed the topic in-depth a few years back. As confident as I was in *not* wanting biological children, his questions made it clear that the door was about to close forever.

"We can freeze your eggs before treatment if that's something you want. Otherwise, the drugs can damage your eggs. If you ever want to get pregnant after this, I can set you up with an appointment in our fertility clinic. But you'll have to make the decision now."

"Nope," I replied without a doubt. "There is no need to freeze my eggs." I empathized with the diagnosed women who wanted children and had to take another step to secure their life-long dream.

"You must get a Multigated Acquisition scan done, otherwise known as a MUGA heart scan, before the Herceptin. One of the drug's most severe side effects is interference with the heart. We must monitor your heart closely throughout the duration. As for other side effects, we can counteract them nowadays with medications. But I will tell you, you *are* going to lose your hair. For liability reasons, I have to inform you that there's a chance your hair may never grow back." My stomach tumbled and dropped. He must have sensed it because he quickly added, "But in all the years I've been doing this, I've never seen that happen."

Feeling only marginally better, I asked, "When do you think I'll start chemo?"

"A few things need to happen first. As I mentioned before, you will need to get a MUGA heart scan done, and you'll need to meet with Rhonda for an orientation to chemotherapy. Then, after that, we can set you up on the schedule for treatment."

I expected there would be necessary steps to properly lead up to starting such an aggressive treatment for such aggressive cancer, but I never thought it would take 22 days. And in 22 days, there still wasn't a start date on my calendar.

* * *

After my appointment with Dr. Santos, I drove to the Moorpark photo studio to tell Ozzy the news face-to-face. I found him sitting in his office in the dark, retouching a tequila bottle that Bruce had photographed for a client—the pale blue light from his three computer monitors wrapped around him like a spaceship's command center. I could sense he was hyper-focused and was reluctant to distract him, but I had waited long enough.

Taking a seat behind him, I opened the conversation with, "I have to tell you something." He swiveled around to face me, his pen tool for retouching still in his hand.

"Sure," he said.

From the look on his face, he didn't suspect anything was wrong. He probably thought I would share a change in the post-production timeline or inform him of new jobs I'd been bidding on.

"I found a lump in my breast and was diagnosed with breast cancer," I said. The blank look on his face told me he was trying to process why I seemed so calm.

Under any other circumstance, talking about my boobs with men, apart from Bruce or a doctor, felt awkward. But my breasts had become such a topic of conversation in the past three weeks that by now, it didn't faze me. It was just another body part like a knee or a shin or a calf—except that this one had a tumor growing inside of it.

"I'm not sure how this will affect me coming to photo shoots. I have to do chemo and will lose my hair, but I plan to work the entire time. Likely from home, behind the scenes."

"Don't worry about the shoots. We can handle them," he said. I knew he was right. Over the years, we'd built a fantastic team that could handle any project without me being there.

"It's important that we keep my illness a secret," I told him. "We need to work, and if clients find out, they might not want to contact me for estimates or to discuss projects."

"I'll keep it a secret," he promised.

But then a smile appeared as he swiveled his chair back around, brought up an online search engine, and started typing something. A moment later, he twisted back. "You need to get a Marie Antoinette wig like this one!" He pointed to a picture of an elaborate oil painting on his middle screen. Marie Antoinette was wearing a tightly pin-curled beehive wig that stood about a foot off her head. Perched on top was a tiny blue satin hat covered in diamonds with feathers jutting out. "If you play this thing right, no one will ever know you're bald."

I was surprised at how hard I laughed, especially from a joke that stemmed from the notion of becoming bald. For a brief moment, as I doubled over with laughter, I was myself again.

Ozzy didn't stop there. Later that evening, I received a text from him with a picture attached of a woman missing eyebrows. Drawn onto her forehead were exaggerated, black wavy lines like confused caterpillars. It was as if a child had discovered a Sharpie permanent marker, found his mother asleep, and decided to get creative.

OZZY: How about these for eyebrows?

No matter how hard I tried to catch my breath, I laughed hysterically as I imagined the Marie Antoinette wig combined with the crazy caterpillar eyebrows. Bruce heard me laughing, and I showed him Ozzy's text. We both fell onto the bed, laughing so hard we had tears in our eyes.

ME: I'll always look pleasantly surprised. I finally texted back.

OZZY: Indeed!

When Ozzy approached my hair loss with humor, the weight felt one hundred pounds lighter. As they say, laughter is the best medicine; truthfully, it was exactly what I needed. When you have cancer, the feeling you get while laughing is the closest to feeling free—*and normal*—again.

THE CANCER-FIGHTING GENE

THREE DAYS LATER, Chris sat beside me in the genetic counselor's office. In my hand was the completed paperwork the counselor had mailed to me before our visit. I'd answered every question about *who* in my immediate and extended family had cancer and *which types* of cancer they had.

It was important for my sister to be there. Not only for emotional support since my chemo orientation would follow but as my biological sister. Was she at high risk of getting breast cancer, too? It was something we needed to know.

After studying my paperwork, the counselor grabbed a sheet of paper from her printer tray and drew a rudimentary family tree. Each leafless tree branch contained the name of a family member who'd had cancer. There were several branches: my mom's oldest brother Don had died from prostate and pancreatic cancer; my mom's other brother Gary was currently battling bladder cancer after prostate; Gary's daughter Tammy had survived stage four lung cancer; and my Granddad Wells lost his fight with lung and brain cancer long before I was born. The branches remained empty on my dad's side of the tree since no one, at least at that time, had been afflicted with cancer. When the counselor finished scribbling the names, she rotated the paper so we could see the tree right side up.

"There doesn't seem to be any breast cancer in your family history. If this is true," she said and tucked her pencil behind her ear, "I think it's doubtful that you are carrying the BRCA1 or BRCA2 gene mutations."

My sister was the straight "A" student who always raised her hand in class if she didn't understand something. "What are the BRCA1 and BRCA2 gene mutations?" she asked, which was the exact thing I was wondering.

"They're the two main gene mutations directly linked to breast cancer. Both impact the overall risk of developing breast cancer in a person's lifetime," the counselor explained. "When the DNA becomes damaged, the genes are no longer effective at fixing the broken DNA that helps to prevent the disease."

"Do you think I should be tested?" Chris asked, concerned.

"Since you're full biological sisters, a family history is a good indicator if there's a mutation present, but no one else in your family has had breast cancer. I have a feeling there aren't any mutations. Let's get your sister tested first." Then she looked directly at me, "If a mutation is present, it may alter your decisions moving forward."

If the test results proved I had it, there'd be a greater chance that even if chemo and radiation were successful against my current tumor, a new mass could appear in either breast. Instead of a lumpectomy, a mastectomy or even a double mastectomy might be the safer route.

"And, if you choose to get tested," she informed my sister, "just know, once that risk is documented, it will likely affect your insurance premiums from that point forward."

How pathetic there might be a price to pay for having knowledge that could save one's life, I thought. *Wouldn't knowing that you have a high risk of getting breast cancer be important for everyone to know? Wouldn't women who knew that they were high risk be more likely to do self-exams and get annual mammograms?*

"Head down to the lab," she added. "They will draw blood and send it off to be tested. I'll call you with the results." As Chris threw her purse strap over her shoulder and walked out, the counselor stopped me before I could reach the doorway. "How are you handling all of this?"

"I'm trying my best to navigate through it," I replied, already exhausted from the stress.

And then she said something I'll never forget, "I hate to tell you, but it's only going to get worse."

My heart galloped. *Worse? What the hell does she mean by that?* And then, she stared at me as if I was supposed to thank her for that ominous and deeply disturbing warning. Like a psychic predicting my future, she seemed to know something that I didn't, and yet, the advice lacked the information I needed to change the outcome. Without knowing what to say and without her saying anything more, I quickly left the room, leaving her and the uncomfortable conversation behind.

"Did you hear what she told me?" I asked my sister in the hallway, completely confused.

My sister was busy looking at the time on her phone. "No, what?"

"That it's only going to get worse."

"What is?" she asked.

"I don't know. What do you think she means by that?"

"Maybe the chemo part?" Chris speculated. "Let's get upstairs to your next appointment. Maybe it'll become clearer as to what she meant."

But on the elevator ride up to the fourth floor, I couldn't imagine *how* the situation could become any worse. I was trapped inside a nightmare. Is it possible to have a nightmare within a nightmare? I felt as if my stamina for surviving cancer had reached its limit.

If it gets any worse, how will I make it through?

As we sat in the oncology department, once again, waiting, I couldn't help but think about the hand-drawn tree and the names of my family members that gave life to its branches. They were all listed: my uncles, cousin, and grandfather. Maybe I didn't know if I had a gene mutation yet, but I already knew something important. I shared genes with these incredibly strong-willed, cancer-fighting relatives. And the fire that was inside of them, to stand up against the disease and not back down, had to be inside of me, too. Even if I was—*or wasn't*—genetically predisposed to getting cancer, I was definitely genetically predisposed to fight like hell.

"Jennifer," the oncology nurse said. "It's time for your orientation."

THE CHEMO ROOM

THE CHEMO ORIENTATION room was small, cluttered, and chaotic. Books were stacked on the floor. Three chairs were angled haphazardly around the small table where pamphlets were scattered. It was as if the last visitors learned about chemo and then said, "screw it!" before tossing aside the reading material and running out. The oncology nurse, Rhonda, quickly scooped up the brochures, put them on a credenza, and told us to take a seat.

Rhonda placed a blue binder on the table in front of me and flipped to the first page. In big black letters, it boasted my name and the words "Chemotherapy Treatment Plan." *This is real. I can't believe I am doing this,* I thought.

"Do you know what chemotherapy is?" Rhonda asked, staring at me with her blue saucer-like eyes shadowed by choppy blonde bangs.

"Not exactly," I replied.

I figured if I said yes, she might skip over something important. Besides, it was good for Chris to hear. She could listen and fill me in if I didn't understand some of the details.

"It's systemic, meaning it impacts your entire body. The drugs target cells that proliferate quickly like skin, hair, bone marrow, intestines, and cancer cells."

I liked the idea that chemo would target my entire system in case cancer had set up camp elsewhere. This was a way to eliminate every last cancer cell and regain control, an important step in creating a cancer-free future, even though the organs she mentioned might get damaged as a sacrifice toward the greater cause.

Rhonda flipped to the next page. It stated that my customized cancer treatment was a disciplined plan that consisted of using one or more anti-cancer drugs, and then it listed four medicines:

1. PERTUZUMAB/PERJETA
2. TRASTUZUMAB/HERCEPTIN
3. DOCETAXEL/TAXOTERE
4. CARBOPLATIN/PARAPLATIN

Perfect, I thought, *the ingredients in my personalized chemo cocktail.*

Below the name of the first drug were the most common side effects when given with Herceptin and chemotherapy. Rhonda began to read the first list out loud, "Diarrhea or constipation, hair loss, fatigue...," but the first drug had such a long list that I skipped ahead and read them to myself more quickly.

MOST COMMON SIDE EFFECTS OF PERJETA:

...HEADACHE, LOW LEVELS OF RED BLOOD CELLS, LOW LEVELS OF WHITE BLOOD CELLS, LOW PLATELET COUNT, MOUTH SORES, NAUSEA, MUSCLE PAIN, VOMITING, WEAKNESS, AND PERIPHERAL NEUROPATHY (TINGLING IN HANDS AND FEET).

With a list this long for one drug, what does that mean for the other three medicines? I thought.

Rhonda stated, "If you cannot zip your jacket from neuropathy, please get in touch with us. Otherwise, feeling numbness in your hands and feet is normal."

Unable to zip my jacket? To Rhonda, it all seemed routine. This was what she saw every day at work. It was what she told patients time and time again. I, on the other hand, had never in a million years considered that the process of killing cancer could make me unable to dress myself.

Before I'd fully processed the neuropathy, Rhonda began to list the potential side effects of Herceptin, Drug #2. "Nausea with or without vomiting, diarrhea, infections, body pain, headache, fatigue, dizziness, shortness of breath, increased cough, swelling and/or scarring of the lungs, low white and red blood cell count." And then she added, "Even though it's rare, this drug can interfere with the pumping of your heart, so we need to take precautions and have heart scans done periodically throughout treatment."

Looking at my sister, pretending as if Rhonda didn't exist, I asked, "How am I supposed to work through all of this?"

Chris looked as if her confidence had deflated. "I don't know," she replied, and I glanced at the clock on the wall. 2:15 p.m. The orientation room was like a time warp where 15 minutes felt like 15 hours.

Rhonda decided it was best to move on, as was proven in her decision to mention more potential side effects, this time for Taxotere. "The third drug listed is an anti-cancer chemotherapy drug." She casually read us the list as if they weren't life-changing. "You may experience nausea, vomiting, diarrhea, excessive tearing, fatigue, dizziness, constipation, loss of appetite, hair loss, nail changes, change in taste, swelling of the hands/feet/legs, numbness/tingling of arms/legs, irregular heartbeat, stomach pain, effects on concentration, it can temporarily affect the number of healthy blood cells in the body with increased risk of infection."

Rhonda finished and looked up at me. My silence made it evident to my sister that I was struggling, so she interjected, "Does that mean her immune system will be compromised?"

"Definitely," Rhonda confirmed. "Her white blood cell count

will be the lowest five to nine days after treatment. Since the recovery time for this drug is twenty-one days, she will need to get an injection to counteract it. No crowds, concerts, large events, or hanging out with small children, if possible." And then she looked directly at me. "We want you to still enjoy life, but adjustments must be made."

Enjoy my life? I knew I was supposed to "embrace the journey," but this journey felt impossible to endure, let alone embrace.

Chris stayed on point. "She needs to walk her dog. Is that still okay?"

"Yes, walking is great exercise," Rhonda confirmed, "but she must wear latex gloves when handling the feces, even when using a bag to pick it up." Rhonda looked over at me. "You'll need to buy a less-abrasive toothpaste and toothbrush to avoid cuts in your gums. You can't afford an infection because any ailment will take longer to heal. Use an electric razor to help with nicks or cuts. Don't walk around barefoot, either. It's too risky."

When I heard the words "barefoot" and "risky" together, I was reminded of a long-forgotten memory of my mom saying, "Put on your flip-flops!" Our neighborhood had a community pool. As kids, we spent most of the summer there swimming. "It'll ruin your entire day if one of you steps on a piece of broken glass. It's not worth the risk."

Mom wasn't wrong, but my sister and I still hurried out of the house without shoes, jumping around to keep the hot pavement from burning our feet. But now, everything seemed too risky. Even if I listened to Mom and wore flip-flops, it couldn't protect me from the number of other things out to "ruin my day."

"Oh, and be sure the foods you eat are fully cooked to avoid bacteria, especially eggs, and beef, and never eat sushi," Rhonda added. *I love sushi.* "Also, be sure to avoid the sun and wear sunscreen." Avoiding the sun in Palm Springs is like avoiding snow in the mountains. With 268 days of sun in Palm Springs a year, the sun was happening whether it was good for me or not. She continued, "Avoid herbal supplements or vitamins unless they are cleared with Dr. Santos. Some might interfere with the effectiveness of your treatment."

The clock read 2:35 p.m.

"Sorry." Rhonda noticed. "We have one last anti-cancer chemotherapy drug to cover. The primary side effects of that drug are nausea and vomiting, taste changes, hair loss, weakness, blood test abnormalities, diarrhea, constipation, among some that are less common," and her voice picked up speed, trying to finish the list before running out of breath, "like mouth sores and abnormal blood liver enzymes, and again, neuropathy," finishing with a quick inhale and then exhale. "Do you have any questions?"

I did. "How will my hair fall out?"

"Patients have told me that it comes out in clumps. You might want to shave your head or cut your hair short before starting chemo. It'll be less traumatic that way." Traumatic or not, I needed to keep my hair intact for as long as possible to minimize the risk that our clients would know my secret. Shaving my head was not an option. "I've heard some women keep a lock of their hair as a keepsake," she offered.

I looked over at my sister and, making sure Rhonda didn't see, rolled my eyes to convey how I felt about the idea. It seemed strange. *Who stores a chunk of dead hair and considers it a keepsake?*

"But here's some good news," she said as her eyes widened, "you can eat whatever you want. It's perfectly okay to enjoy milkshakes, cheeseburgers, or even pizza. Whatever it is that you're hungry for, you should eat. It's important to keep your weight up."

And now, keeping a chunk of dead hair didn't seem as strange as a healthcare professional encouraging a greasy, high-calorie, fatty diet. The path ahead was no longer about wellness but survival.

"You might also experience chemo brain, otherwise known as chemo fog," Rhonda stated. "It's a cognitive impairment that normally goes away once the treatments are finished."

Again, *how will I work?*

The next page started a new section titled "Methods to Implement Infusions." Completely overwhelmed, I wanted to leave. 2:41 p.m.

"So there are three choices on how to receive your infusions." Rhonda took a sip of water. "First, a standard IV. But I must warn you, after prolonged use, the vein can collapse." *Nope!* "An implantable port requires a minor out-patient surgery but is more convenient and pain-free during treatments." *I wouldn't say I liked the idea of surgery, but I liked the concept of not experiencing pain.* "The third option is a PICC line in which a central catheter is inserted into the vein of your arm. The only downfall is that it remains in your arm, covered when not in use." *How will I keep my secret alive with a device taped to my arm? Summer is coming, and I need to wear short sleeves.*

"I'll take the port," I said.

Rhonda seemed taken aback that I had formed a decision so quickly. "Don't you need time to consider your options?"

My sister was trying to picture me—with a port—in Jamaica. "Will she be able to swim with a port?" Snorkeling in the Caribbean was something I'd been looking forward to after hearing that the water is crystal clear and warm.

Rhonda confirmed I could swim with one.

"I'll take the port!" I told her again. I was confident in my decision.

When the clock hit 2:52 p.m., I reached for my bag to signal that the time was up. I didn't want to hear about one more discouraging side effect or ailment. But before we could escape, Rhonda had another dreadful activity for us to do.

"I'd like to walk you through the infusion room where you'll get treatments," she told me.

The chemo room? Was she going to take us on a field trip through the chemo room? Right now?

Unfortunately, yes.

Officially a student of chemotherapy, I heaved the blue binder up under my arm as Chris and I followed Rhonda down a short hallway. Stopping in front of a large set of double doors with rectangular windows, I tried to peek inside but could only see the opposite wall.

Before pressing the button to open the heavy doors, Rhonda turned to me and asked, "Are you ready?"

"Yes," I responded, even though I wasn't. I knew the question was rhetorical, a way to prepare me for what was coming.

The doors swung back, and we stepped inside. At least 20 over-stuffed leather recliners lined the perimeter of the room. A patient sat in every chair, tubes stuffed into their veins or ports. It was impossible not to notice the headscarves, wigs, and hats resting on their presumably bald heads. They were of all ages, in various stages of their treatments, and at different stages of life. Regardless of gender, age, or background, cancer does not discriminate.

I bowed my head to avoid eye contact. Not only was it tough to face my new reality, but I didn't want to look for too long out of respect for their privacy. I watched my shoes as I took steps further into the room—right and then left, right and then left—silencing my footsteps by stepping lightly.

"Pretend that you're walking on glass," my ballet instructor told me as a child. "Imagine the soles of your feet barely touching the floor." Treading softly, however, didn't change the fact that we were intruding on these people during the worst time of their lives.

As we walked in further, it felt like the place was filled with misery, sadness, and defeat. I inhaled deeply, trying not to become emotional, and could smell urine mixed with antiseptic. It was warm, so I tugged on the collar of my T-shirt. I needed fresh air, the kind that didn't reek of disease.

At the back was another room, with ten more beige recliners. More headscarves, more wigs, more bald heads, and more hats.

Rhonda told us, "Next to every treatment chair, there's a single chair for a guest. You can bring one visitor with you at a time. We keep it minimal to prevent germs."

My sister whispered, "I'll always come with you."

I was surprised that she volunteered to be my chemo sidekick. Maybe she was too protective of her younger sister to send me there alone. Like sleeping in the same bed as children after watching a horror flick, scary things were better when faced together. But the truth was, I had to be there; she didn't.

All I could think about on our drive home was how I was about to become a chemo patient. *This is my life now.*

My sister must have had her own conflicting and discouraging thoughts. Not once did she try to make conversation or turn on the radio. She had also crashed hard into her new reality. Just like the people sitting in that dreadful room, her little sister was about to become one of them.

Embrace the journey, I reminded myself. *Try and embrace the journey.*

WHAT IS COURAGE?

ONE YEAR AFTER FINISHING TREATMENT, I trained to become a mentor to help women and men navigate their own breast cancer journeys. During one of my weekly calls, a woman who was about to start chemotherapy told me over the phone, "I have long red hair, and my identity has always been tied to it. People comment on it. Compliment it. I am proud of it. It is the one thing about my appearance that makes me truly unique. I won't feel like me without it."

Hair may be associated with vanity, but it also signifies something much more profound. It makes us, us. Not that hair loss is easy for men either, but society is accustomed to seeing men bald. As women, many of us view our hair as an essential part of our femininity, and even more so, society as a whole expects us to have it.

When I returned home from my initial tour of the chemo room, a box was at our doorstep. Bruce was working in the kitchen and hadn't noticed it had been delivered. Nonplussed that he could have easily seen the shipping address was from a wig company, I grabbed the package, unlocked the door, and hid it under my jacket.

"Welcome back," he yelled as I rushed through the living room. "What's inside the box?"

"Just a pair of new sandals I ordered." I hated to lie, but I needed time to figure out if I could get used to wearing a wig before I showed it to anyone else, even my husband.

In our bedroom, I ripped open the box and pulled out a cellophane bag containing a squished, dishwater-blonde wig. I placed the wig on my fist to let it hang naturally, hoping it might "fluff up." Turning my wrist back and forth, it looked like the wig was shaking its head no. *I couldn't agree more, Lady Wig. I'm not feeling this either.*

I drummed up enough courage to put it on. Scooting the bangs into position, I wiggled the netting back and forth to find a comfortable fit and stared at my new reflection. A strange doppelgänger with the same eyes, nose, and chin stared back at me. It was me, but a version I had never met.

I spent a few minutes trying to acclimate. I shifted the shiny bangs down to cover more of my forehead. It felt like doll hair, and when I tried to move a strand here or there, it slid right back to where it was before. No matter how many times I shifted, rotated, or combed the fake strands, they popped back into position as if they'd been programmed at the wig factory. Not only did *Lady Wig* make me feel like a peculiar life-sized Barbie, but it was also heavy, uncomfortable, hot, and itchy.

There are a lot of things I'd rather spend $280 on. The store had a return policy, but I knew that once I shipped it back, there was no way I'd order a replacement. This was it. I'd either wear this wig or none at all. *Give it a chance,* I thought.

After ten minutes of hating it, I took it off, clipped it onto a pant hanger, and shoved it into the back of my closet behind some formal dresses I hadn't worn in years and probably no longer fit.

I remembered what my cousin Tammy had said, "When it came down to it, I preferred wearing headscarves. It was much more comfortable."

I had a bin full of scarves and pulled out a soft grey one. I carefully wrapped it around my head. *Nope.* I tried on a silk scarf with a vibrant floral pattern. *Nope.* Even the scarf that matched my current hair color, looked off.

Leaving the wig and scarves behind, I got in my car and drove to Target in hopes of finding a better solution. I needed some household items anyway, so it wouldn't be a wasted trip if I couldn't find something suitable at the department store. When I walked through the automatic doors, a section of seasonal summer hats hung directly in front of me. *Yep, 269 days of sun a year.*

I grabbed a plain black cap from the rack and put it on. It felt comfortable on my head. I liked that it didn't promote a specific sports team or brand name. At the jewelry counter mirror, I looked at my reflection and smiled because the reflection was me.

This is it. I found my new identity.

I went to the check stand. For less than ten bucks, I was ready for the start of treatment and what might follow.

The cashier asked, "Would you like to wear this out?" She didn't want the bill of the cap to get crushed.

"Sure," I told her, planting it securely on my head.

In the parking lot, after stuffing my bags in the trunk, I got in the car and glanced in the visor's mirror to examine the new accessory from different angles. Although I couldn't go to fancy restaurants with a sporty ball cap on, I figured I could wear it everywhere else. Besides that, with all of the expected chemo side effects in the near future, it didn't seem possible to visit fine dining establishments anyway.

As I drove home, I thought about how difficult my life was about to become. Difficult to work. Difficult to endure side effects.

Difficult to stay strong. I needed the courage to get me through. *Not some courage, but a lot.* And then I thought about how cancer patients are often described as being courageous. I didn't feel courageous at all. In fact, there wasn't an ounce of courage inside of me. If anything, I felt weak and cowardly.

"You are so courageous," I'd told Krista six months ago after she shared the details of her breast cancer battle with me, which was the truth, but it was also easy to say when at a loss for words. A few days later, I'd shared my concern for Krista's failing health with Mae and ended the conversation with, "If I should ever get diagnosed with cancer, I hope I am as courageous as she is."

And now, here I am, hoping—and searching—for courage. I needed the courage to walk back into the chemo room and climb into that recliner. With an urgency to find some courage or at least learn how to manifest it, I did an online search for the definition of "courage" when I got home.

To truly understand certain things, it has always helped me to dissect them. If I break down the word into parts and see how they connect, it's easier for me to grasp what something really means. What I discovered was insightful. The Latin root of "courage" is "cor," meaning "heart."

If having courage comes from the heart, then courage must be associated with love, I thought. And then, *like love, it is something that can't be forced.*

I had an epiphany:

Before each chemo treatment, I will think about a person, alive or deceased, who I love tremendously. Out of my love for them, I'll find the courage to go on. Every chemo treatment will be dedicated to someone special. If courage and love are intertwined, I will focus on my loved ones to give me strength.

This idea made perfect sense in a world that no longer made sense to me. I'd channel love to create courage. And, after all, falling in love is pretty courageous, too.

I AM NOT A DIAGNOSIS

UTAIWAN, who was in THE SECRET SOCIETY and was also one of my sister's bridesmaids, called and was enthusiastic about sharing, "I have already saved a thousand dollars for Jamaica."

It was a big deal. She was halfway there. The cost of the trip secured a luxury room, all meals prepared by a private chef, and unlimited cocktails in the gorgeous beachfront villa my sister and David had rented for the week.

"That's amazing!" I said, proud of her.

But then the excitement dropped from her voice. "May I ask you something?"

"Anything," I replied as I looked down to see Stella next to me, ready for her walk.

"Do you think you'll be able to make it to Christine and David's wedding?"

I thought back to Nietzsche. *He who has a why to live can bear almost any how.*

"I will be there, even if I have to be wheeled in on a gurney," I said convincingly, which made her laugh.

But honestly, I wasn't sure. If I couldn't use a regular toothbrush or walk barefoot, how would my immune system handle eight hours of recycled cabin air on the plane ride? With fatigue and nausea, how would I have the energy to participate in all the wedding festivities?

When I hung up, I grabbed Stella's leash to take her on a walk. As she sniffed patches of grass, I dialed my sister, excited to tell her that people were preparing for her wedding. *Her wedding isn't trite, see? It's brilliant and happening.*

But when I shared the news with my sister, her response was silence on the other end. "Isn't it incredible?" I asked, fishing for the expected response I thought I would hear.

"Sure," she said, and that was it.

"Everything okay?" I asked. When she didn't immediately respond, I looked down at the screen of my phone to see if the call was dropped. It wasn't.

"Sis," Chris finally said, "we are considering pushing out our wedding a year."

Although I already knew the reason, I panicked and asked, "How come?"

"I want you to be there as my Matron of Honor."

Completely thrown off, sad, and in disbelief, I stuttered, "I don't want you... I don't want you to... I don't want you to have to do that." As I finished getting the words out, a cloud simultaneously moved across the sun, darkening my entire neighborhood and muting the vibrant colors around me. Bright yellow flowers turned a dull shade of mustard. Verdant grass became the shade of evergreen. The bright pink and orange blossoms of the many bougainvilleas were practically colorless. It was as if the whole neighborhood, at that moment, was somehow filled with my sadness.

But it was her sisterly duty to convince me that pushing the wedding out was ideal. "We live together anyway," her voice now upbeat, "so why does it matter? David agrees. I want you to feel well enough to stand up with me."

"The save-the-dates were sent out. People are saving up. You've waited your entire life for this," I said, discouraging her.

"Just think about it," she reiterated. "You know better than anyone whether you'll feel good enough to go. I want you to be there, and if that means waiting, we're fine with it."

A wave of guilt plummeted over me. "I can't be the cause of postponing your wedding." The thought made me sick to my stomach.

"One favor to ask," she said before hanging up, "please let us know sooner than later so we can update the guests before they start making travel arrangements," and I agreed.

As we ended the call, with Stella doing her best to keep up, I darted up the sidewalk to our front gate. Inside, I collapsed onto my bed, my shirt wet with tears, as if I had been caught in a downpour.

Why is this happening?

If it were up to me, they wouldn't change the date. But it wasn't up to me. It was up to my cancer. Cancer wasn't just holding me hostage, but all of us. We were controlled by it. A few malignant cells had changed everything.

After several rounds of sobbing, I started to think about the situation from a different perspective. My sister had paid me the biggest compliment of my life. Her sacrifice was proof of how much she loved me. How important it was for me to be there. And the fact that David was willing to change it, too, for me, made me feel incredibly loved. This feeling made me want to address her request even more.

I grabbed a pen and my journal. On a page, I wrote: TO POSTPONE OR NOT POSTPONE—THAT IS THE QUESTION. Without having my first chemotherapy yet, I wasn't even sure how my body would respond, but I knew the pros and cons.

PROS FOR POSTPONING THE WEDDING:

• I WILL HAVE ADEQUATE TIME TO DEAL WITH THE CHEMO, FOCUSING ON THE TREATMENT PLAN WITHOUT ANY TIME CONSTRAINTS.

• MY HAIR WILL FALL OUT, BUT HOPEFULLY, IT WILL GROW BACK. I'LL HAVE HAIR WHEN SHE SAYS, "I DO," AND WILL FEEL LIKE MYSELF AGAIN.

CONS FOR POSTPONING THE WEDDING:

• WHAT IF A CATASTROPHIC EVENT CAUSES THE NEW DATE TO BE PUSHED OUT EVEN FURTHER? THEN WHAT?

• WHAT IF SOMEONE ELSE IN THE FAMILY GROWS ILL DURING THE NEXT YEAR? WHAT IF IT IS ONE OF DAVID'S PARENTS OR HIS BROTHER? THEY WOULD HAVE MISSED DAVID'S BIG MOMENT BECAUSE OF ME.

• IF I AM LUCKY ENOUGH TO BECOME CANCER-FREE, HOW DO I KNOW THE CANCER WON'T RETURN? RECURRENCES HAPPEN. I'D HAVE TO START ALL OVER AGAIN, LANDING IN THE SAME SITUATION.

So much was at stake as I studied the options. Without clarity, I called my mom for advice. But after I told her what had happened, another unexpected thing occurred. For the first time since my diagnosis, I heard her cry.

To hear her cry felt worse than when I cried. I could feel her internal struggle: her first-born daughter was willing to change the biggest celebration of her life for her youngest, who was sick with a life-threatening disease that required a significant amount of time to treat. As I listened to her break down, I wanted to fix it. I wanted to fix her and my sister's wedding. I wanted to fix the chaos that I had created.

"I'm sorry," was all I could say as I listened to more heavy breaths of sorrow.

Finally, she replied in a comforting voice, "It's not your fault. No one blames you."

And with all that transpired, from my sister's incredible and thoughtful sacrifice to my mom's heartbreaking sadness, my guilt pivoted to anger. It was intense, and it was the first time I'd felt this level of indignation in my journey. For 28 days, cancer had put us in a chokehold. It disrupted each of our lives. And its destruction wasn't going to stop until I stopped it.

I have to take a stand against it. Take back my power. I must protect them.

The only thing I knew to do, was to contact Dr. Santos and get his professional advice. With my fingers pounding the keys, I wrote an email to him in hopes that he could help.

DR. SANTOS,

I AM GETTING A PORT PUT IN ON JUNE 2 AND STARTING CHEMO ON JUNE 6. MY SISTER IS GETTING MARRIED NEXT YEAR, ON MAY 5, AND I'M UNSURE IF I WILL BE ABLE TO MAKE IT. THE WEDDING IS IN JAMAICA, SO IT'S ESSENTIAL THAT I CAN FLY ON A PLANE AND BE AWAY FROM TREATMENTS FOR A WEEK. AT THIS POINT, SHE IS THINKING ABOUT PUSHING THEIR WEDDING OUT SO I CAN ATTEND. PLEASE PROVIDE SOME HONEST ADVICE. WHAT'S THE CHANCE OF ME GETTING TO JAMAICA IN A LITTLE OVER 11 MONTHS? IS IT POSSIBLE TO WORK MY TREATMENTS AROUND THAT TRIP? ANY INSIGHT WOULD BE GREATLY APPRECIATED.

SINCERELY,

JENNIFER

Even after the email was sent, the rage continued to race through me. Pushing back my chair, I yelled, "Fuck you, cancer!" And then I screamed at the top of my lungs. No words, just a loud, high-pitched release of emotion.

Although I never allow anger to control me, for the first time in my life, I wanted to punch a wall or kick something. I jumped up and down, overcome by the intense energy. I ran around the house as if being chased by something savage. After so much jumping and running, I finally stopped, took some deep breaths, and realized that succumbing to the anger wasn't making me feel any better.

Get a grip, I told myself.

Back at my desk, I tried to focus on work. It was extremely difficult at first, my mind wouldn't let it go, but I eventually became distracted enough for the rage to subside. After an hour or so, I received a response from Dr. Santos' office.

DEAR JENNIFER,

THE FIRST SIX CYCLES OF TREATMENT ARE CHEMOTHERAPY. SINCE THEY ARE THREE WEEKS APART, YOU SHOULD BE DONE WITH CHEMO-THERAPY BY SEPTEMBER OF THIS YEAR. SURGERY IS USUALLY PERFORMED A MONTH LATER. AFTER COMPLETING THE SIXTH CYCLE, YOU WILL BE ON HERCEPTIN, A MONOCLONAL ANTIBODY. MONOCLONAL ANTIBODY INFU-SIONS ARE SIMILAR TO RECEIVING HORMONAL THERAPY. THAT SAID, AS LONG AS YOU ARE IN GOOD HEALTH, BEING ON HERCEPTIN WILL NOT MAKE YOU MISS YOUR TRIP. WHEN THE TIME COMES, YOUR ONCOLOGY NURSE CAN RESCHEDULE YOUR TREATMENT TO A DATE AFTER YOU RETURN. I HOPE THIS HELPS.

RAINA (ON BEHALF OF DR. SANTOS)

The nurse's words were tantamount to watching a rainbow stretch across the sky after a storm. A poetic promise of hope. My sister's wedding was going to happen—on schedule—and Raina's advice was the closest thing to a guarantee.

Yes, I will be there.

I immediately dialed my sister. When she answered, I yelled with enthusiasm, "You don't have to push out your wedding date!"

"What made you decide that?" She seemed skeptical.

I read Raina's response to her, delightfully clinging to the sound of every syllable, ending with, "It's official! You're getting married next May!"

With deafening excitement, she yelled to David, "We're getting married as planned!" I heard his voice in the background, and then she answered him by saying, "Yes, she will be able to make it!"

On that day, after 28 days of feeling victimized, I realized:

I am not a diagnosis. A disease cannot define me. I am bigger than my physical body and any physical ailment. My spirit, my soul, the real me, the true self, extends beyond limitations and boundaries. I am bigger than emotional turmoil. Bigger than illness. My spirit is undeterred by the human body. With a sudden rush of adrenaline, I thought, *it's now "me" against "it."*

FEISTY RIGHTY

With the realization that the "me" was separate from the "it," I no longer claimed ownership of the tumor. It was an evil villain that just happened to reside inside my right breast. Instead of saying, "MY cancer," the tumor required a proper name. That way, when I referred to it, there would be a clear distinction between my healthy, thriving body and the opponent.

When it came to naming inanimate things, Beth came to mind. In high school, we amused ourselves by coming up with clever, alliterative names for mundane things. Mushrooms received titles like "Betty the Button" and "Enya the Enoki." An old pipe was named "Duke." We were so entertained by this game that we still talked about it years later.

And so...

ME: Will you help me name the tumor? I texted.

BETH: Name what?

ME: Will you help me name the cancerous tumor in my breast?

There was a brief pause, and then...

BETH: WHAT ABOUT CUP HUSTLER OR BUSTIER HERMIT SINCE IT LIKES TO HIDE?

ME: TROUBLED TATA?

BETH: LUMPY LOUIS?

ME: DO YOU THINK THE TUMOR IS A GIRL OR A BOY?

BETH: MAYBE GENDER-NEUTRAL?

ME: IN THAT CASE, BOBBI BOOB?

BETH: WHAT A DUNCE, THAT BOBBI, A REAL BOOB!

ME: WHAT ABOUT FEISTY RIGHTY?

BETH: FEISTY RIGHTY. I LIKE IT!

ME: ME TOO.

And that is how it happened and why the book is titled *Feisty Righty*. "Feisty" made sense since the tumor was aggressive, and "Righty" identified the tumor's choice of locations.

There was something unexpectedly empowering about naming the tumor. Not only had I separated myself from cancer, but *Feisty Righty* also had weaknesses. All villains do. Plus, creating a proper name for it brought light-heartedness to the situation. Of course, Ozzy's Marie Antoinette photo was hilarious, but that was him poking fun at what was happening. For me to step back enough to find the humor myself meant I had come further along in my journey. From accepting I had cancer by looking at my breast, to building THE SECRET SOCIETY, to trusting my instincts and defining courage, I had—on some level—grown.

* * *

Of course, *Feisty Righty* was the unwelcome guest that accompanied me everywhere. It slept with me in bed. We watched episodes of *Friends* together. It waited with me in long grocery store lines. On occasion, it'd pinch me, reminding me that it was still there and as feisty as ever.

On the day of my first MUGA heart scan, the little villain rode with me to the medical center. I checked in with the receptionist and followed her directions to locate room 130. Navigating the labyrinth of corridors, I couldn't help but notice how drab and generic the place was. The walls were all painted cream, and the carpet was a concrete-block gray. The framed pictures had only slight variations: a flock of birds in one, a slightly different flock of birds with more dandelions in another.

Halfway down the corridor, a sign jutted from the wall that read, "Nuclear Medicine." *At least I don't have to go in there. My life isn't that bad,* I thought. For a moment, I felt empathy for those who had it worse than me. But that moment quickly passed when I noticed the room number on the door: 130.

Of course! Just. My. Luck.

I'd never heard of "nuclear medicine" before. I was aware of nuclear energy, nuclear bombs, and nuclear reactors but never heard the word used to describe a specialized type of medicine. Everything associated with the word "nuclear" seemed incredibly dangerous.

When I entered the waiting room, there wasn't a single person in it. Not even an employee sitting behind the desk. *Where is everyone?*

There were bold signs posted:

NO EATING IN NUCLEAR MEDICINE

TURN OFF YOUR CELL PHONE

THIS ROOM MAY CONTAIN RADIATION

After staring at the ominous signage for 15 minutes, all alone, I felt forgotten. As soon as I stood up to go back out and check with the receptionist, a door swung open, and a man wearing an over-sized lab coat asked me to come with him.

I followed him down the hallway to another door with two more signs:

CAUTION: RADIOACTIVE MATERIALS INSIDE

HAZARDOUS

As he punched a code into a keypad, I half-expected to see a bottomless pit of uranium inside and was relieved to see nothing more than a single chair, a medical cart, and empty bookshelves.

Across from me, another sign hung on the wall:

LET THE STAFF KNOW IF YOU ARE PREGNANT

He saw me staring at it and was obligated to ask, "Are you pregnant?"

"No."

"Do you think that you might be?"

"No."

"Is this your first MUGA heart scan?"

"Yes."

"The doctor will order more MUGA heart scans to be done throughout your Herceptin. I'll give you an IV to withdraw a small amount of blood before mixing it with a tracer made with radioactive material. The tracer binds your red blood cells and will allow me to see how well the blood pumps through your heart. It'll take twenty minutes for the two to mix, so I'll have you wait outside while that happens. After the twenty minutes are up, you'll come back inside so I can reinsert your blood with the tracer in it through the IV." *It's going to be reinserted?!* "Make a fist," he advised and stuck the needle into my vein. Blood filled the tube.

In the secondary waiting room, which I swear was a closet that had been converted by removing the racks and adding three chairs and a tiny table topped with brochures, I (along with *Feisty Righty*) sat down to wait.

NO MOBILE PHONES PERMITTED

The wellness brochures appeared overly handled, and I hadn't brought a book, so I counted 18 moles on my left arm, minus one, which was a sunspot. Finally, 20 minutes had passed.

The man invited me back into the room and inserted the

radioactive blood mixture into my vein. He then removed the IV and placed a bandage over my arm.

"Okay," he said, "it's time to monitor your heart."

He walked me back to a larger room with a massive machine and two treadmills. I had to lie on the machine's table, flat on my back, as he stuck white patches on my chest to hook me up.

"How does this scan work?" I asked.

"A camera uses gamma rays to watch the tracer as it moves through your bloodstream and pumps through your heart. You must remain still."

With all the mammograms and biopsies, I had become an expert in holding still. One *Healing Light Meditation* later, my first MUGA heart scan was over. Another unknown, known.

* * *

After Rhonda had informed me that chemotherapy was about to destroy my immune system and I'd need to use a less-abrasive toothpaste and toothbrush to avoid cuts in my gums, I figured while my immune system was robust, I'd go to the dentist to get my teeth cleaned. So after killing a few hours at a coffee shop, I headed over to the dental office for my appointment.

With a file folder in her hand, Lori, the hygienist, asked the same question she'd asked me every time I'd come to get my check-up for the past twenty years, "Has anything changed with your health since your last visit?"

Half-joking, I said, "Do you have thirty minutes to spare?"

"What happened?"

After an abbreviated version of *what now felt like the same old story*, I finished with, "I was diagnosed with breast cancer."

"I'm so sorry to hear that," she said. "My sister is a seventeen-year breast cancer survivor and is still going strong."

In all the years I had visited Lori, our conversations never went beyond small talk. The weather was always too hot, too cold, or our commutes too long. The most personal thing mentioned was whether her son was on break from school or at summer camp. I was impressed that my story prompted her to say something profound about her life in exchange. But that's what cancer is, on every level, personal.

While removing tartar from my teeth, she shared the details of her sister's diagnosis. It was nice to hear a caregiver's perspective, and I knew if my chemo sidekick was there, she could relate. I only hoped that my own sister would one day tell someone she hardly knew, "My sister is a seventeen-year breast cancer survivor," and be equally as proud.

Once my teeth were polished and flossed, she opened the drawer full of free dental handouts, grabbed a toothbrush and a single metal spool of floss, and offered them to me.

"Here, please have these," she told me as she placed them into my hands.

I thanked her.

But then, she dove back into the stash, pulling out another toothbrush. "You can never have enough."

"I normally only get one, so thanks again!"

But she didn't stop there. Out came another three spools of floss, which she crammed into my already-full hands.

"You'll be in my prayers," she stated as she carefully placed a tiny box of travel-sized toothpaste on top. It teetered like a see-saw. "I'll be thinking of you."

It was evident from the numerous freebies that Lori felt sorry for me. It was her way of sympathizing with spools of floss, tooth-brushes, and a tiny tube of toothpaste that I probably couldn't use anyway because it was too abrasive.

As I walked out of the dental office into the warm afternoon sun, I turned and looked back at the tinted window. As strange as it might sound, I felt sentimental. I would typically be back in six months for another cleaning. But with my upcoming cancer treatments, I wasn't sure when I'd return. Before my next appointment, *Feisty Righty* would have to be obliterated, my immune system repaired, and the cancer journey mostly behind me.

Teeth cleaning now felt like a luxury.

FORGOTTEN LUXURIES

Heeding my surgeon's advice after my outpatient port surgery to take a bath instead of a shower, at home, I slipped into the warm water, careful to keep the bandage that stretched from my collarbone to the top of my left breast dry. The final step before chemotherapy was completed, which felt nothing short of a miracle.

I leaned back against the porcelain tub and watched the soapy bubbles drift along the water's surface. Some attached themselves to others, forming translucent honeycombs, while others popped and disappeared. Between the soothing temperature of the water and being consumed by something as simple—*and as tranquil*—as watching bubbles float around me, I wondered why I'd stopped taking baths.

It's been years since I've taken one. I used to love baths enough to take them once a week. Why did I stop?

It was hard to admit, but I knew why I had stopped. Life had become too busy for baths. Showers were quick. In a world filled with deadlines, constant demands, and exhaustion from the daily grind, there wasn't enough time to lounge in a bubble bath. Life's simple luxuries had been cast aside, and the worst part was ... *I am the one who had chosen to let them go.*

And it wasn't just baths. Even on vacation, the two weeks I'd given myself permission to relax and escape, I'd drag my work with me. In Barcelona, Spain, when everyone was sound asleep in our apartment after a full day of sightseeing, I had crawled out of bed, turned on a desk lamp in the living room, and worked on job estimates, worried we'd lose a client if I didn't. When friends, family, or acquaintances had problems, even when I felt completely depleted, I'd give them my immediate attention and do everything I could to lift them up. Their well-being was always more important than my own.

This is the me that I had created over the years. And as I soaked in that luxurious bath, I finally allowed myself to explore why I'd become this person. Perhaps it was out of perceived necessity, a fear that if I wasn't doing everything I could, in every moment to financially survive, I wouldn't. Or maybe the sound of my voice saying, "No," made me uncomfortable. Not giving someone what they want is disappointing to them, and I didn't like knowing I'd disappointed anyone. Maybe I had grown so accustomed to putting myself second that I actually forgot what it felt like to put myself first. Or worse, the pleasure of putting myself first wasn't as satisfying as the discomfort that came from setting boundaries.

Cruising recklessly through life, ignoring the warning signs, I wouldn't change directions even though a dangerous cliff was up ahead. Tragically, it took a cancer diagnosis and recent port surgery, along with a doctor-encouraged bubble bath, to make me want to step on the brakes and choose a different—*and safer* —route.

It's my responsibility to acknowledge what I need. Take the necessary steps to regain balance, especially since my first chemo is only three days away.

Putting off self-care had to stop, and this bath, which lasted much longer than I anticipated, was the turning of a new leaf. I wasn't sure how I'd change, but it couldn't possibly be more difficult than facing a life-threatening illness.

It was time. Time to put my health and well-being above everything else. Time to shut the cancer down. Time to begin the real battle, even though the battle felt as if it had been going on for years.

Whose love will give me the courage to walk through the double doors, into that dreadful room, and climb into that recliner? Who should I dedicate my first treatment to in order to make it through?

An incredible person—whom I love dearly—came to mind. That person was my Uncle Don.

And then a smile spread across my face as I thought, *Feisty Righty, you have no idea what's coming.*

PART TWO
COURAGE

SHUTTING THE CANCER DOWN

It was finally time to shut the cancer down.

On June 6, at 7:15 a.m., 36 days after my diagnosis, the oncology department was gradually waking up. Chris and I sat in the dimly lit waiting room across from the two other people there —a middle-aged couple who spoke to each other in French. Although my French was limited to what little I retained from my three years in high school, I appreciated the challenge, and distraction, of trying to understand what they were saying.

The silver-haired man mumbled to his wife, "Je suis nerveux." *I am nervous.*

She rested her head on his shoulder, whispering, "Tout ira bien." *It'll be okay.* He squeezed her hand tightly. Even though we didn't share the same native language, we shared the desire to believe that it would, in fact, be okay.

Down the hallway, the chemo room loomed beyond the set of double doors like a portal to a universe of doubt and depression. Through love for my Uncle Don, my mom's oldest brother, I knew I'd need to channel the courage to walk through them and take a seat in my chemo chair. My long-awaited first treatment was for him, a valiant fighter of both prostate and pancreatic cancer.

Don was in his late thirties when I was born. By then, he'd already fallen in love with my aunt. They remained married for over 50 years until his battle to survive cancer finally ended in 2015. He was a man of integrity, intelligence and a notorious prankster.

"The inside of this cover feels like velvet," he'd say to us as children, holding open a hardback book. As soon as we placed our hands on the surface, which, as it turns out, felt nothing like velvet, he'd smack the cover down, sandwiching our hands inside. He'd laugh hysterically as the corners of his mouth creased into his mustache. At four and six years old, Chris and I didn't see the humor in his prank. But now, we wished he was around to try and fool us again.

"Jennifer!" A nurse called out.

With a backpack, laptop, phone charger, notebook, and journal, I was prepared for the next eight hours. My sister had her own supplies stashed inside a brown leather duffel bag filled with bridal magazines.

We didn't pause at the double doors as we had during the orientation. I was in, all in, for whatever was about to happen. When we stepped inside the room, I sighed with relief. Every recliner sat empty.

Good, I thought. *I can acclimate before being surrounded by sick people.*

"The first thing you will need to do when you arrive," the nurse instructed, "is to weigh in." She motioned me to a nearby scale.

Handing the extra weight of my supplies to my sister, I stepped up on the platform without concern for the final number. Whether I had gained or lost weight, I'd soon be starting the "Chemo Diet." Weight loss was inevitable. In fact, I hoped I wouldn't drop pounds too quickly, exposing the secret and prompting people to ask me why.

"One-forty-five," the nurse stated as she jotted the number down and pointed to a recliner in the corner of the room.

Uncle Don, this is for you.

I sat back in the recliner, stuffed the sterile-smelling white pillow into the crease of the armrest, and turned my attention to the tray table that held the television's remote control and a cup holder. There were knobs on the chair to make it sit upright or recline back. My feet moved upwards as a footrest appeared. *It's official; I'm flying first class on Chemo Airlines,* I thought as my sister took her economy seat to my right.

After a long sip from her *Life is Good* mug, the nurse started the computer to check me in. "I see your bloodwork was done yesterday morning," she said after a loud swallow of coffee. "Did you take your anti-nausea medicine and allergy pills?" I nodded. "Great! I will give you another anti-nausea pill now. What would you like to drink? Apple juice, water, or orange juice?"

"I'll take a water."

The French couple entered the room, and his nurse recorded his weight before directing him to a recliner across from us. It felt comforting to know that I wasn't the only person starting chemo that day. When I smiled at the French man, he tilted his head and smiled back.

The nurse's gaze narrowed in on the collar of my shirt. "I see you have a port," she said, examining the puffy white bandage covering the bump about an inch under my collarbone.

"Yes, I had surgery four days ago." It still seemed too new—*too sore*—to use.

"Let me peel away the bandages to check it," she said.

As each bandage was removed, I felt a cool breeze brushing across the stitches. I watched my sister's face for a reaction. *How bad is it?* I thought.

Genuinely surprised, Chris said, "It looks good!"

"It does." The nurse agreed.

Without the ability to see the wound myself, I gently traced my fingertips over it. The strange bump stuck out of my chest a half-inch and felt like a "Lego" had been buried beneath my skin.

"Would you like some numbing spray while I access it?" I nodded several times quickly.

"Spray!" she yelled out to the other nurse, who hurried over to assist with a small metal can. As soon as the ice-cold substance hit my skin, she inserted the needle into the port.

For the next ten minutes, while we waited for the pharmacy to fill the requested medicine, my sister and I observed the room's activity. More patients walked in, weighed in, and took their seats. One patient poked around a basket of crackers until she found a packet of wheat ones. By the look of her curly-haired wig, she was a regular.

How can one room contain so much misery? I thought.

My nurse returned carrying a plastic bin filled with two clear bags of medicine. "We'll start with the Perjeta," she informed me, "which will take about sixty minutes. The Herceptin will be next, which will take another hour." Clamping the Perjeta onto the IV pole, she connected it to my port, and the medicine ran through my veins.

As the first bag emptied, the only thing I felt was the sudden urge to pee. Still tethered to the pole, Chris helped me to the restroom, rolling the pole behind me.

"How are you feeling?" the nurse asked, checking in when I returned to my seat.

"Good," I told her.

"Would you like me to show you how to use the television?"

"I'm okay without it. It's nice having time with my sister."

In our early forties, we rarely spent a solid eight hours together, even on the weekend. Life was busy for both of us. But now, there were wedding plans to be made, and judging by the stack of bridal magazines resting on Chris' lap, it was time to hunt for ideas.

She handed me a magazine. I smiled as I stared down at the cover showing a bouquet of white and purple hydrangeas. When I married Bruce in July 2004, it was our wedding flower. It's incredible how wedding dress styles change and decorations come and go, but flowers are forever in fashion.

"What type of flowers do you want?" I asked.

Flipping through a magazine, carefully examining the details on each page, she said, "Something with orchids. Did you know Jamaica has over two hundred species of orchids?" *Orchids are timeless, too.*

"Sounds amazing," I replied, imagining a tropical island covered in them. "What type of wedding dress do you want?" I looked down at an advertisement. A model wore a puffy white ballgown reminiscent of Cinderella's.

"Something formal. Jamaica is humid, so I need a dress for that climate. Nothing too hot."

After the second bag of medicine shriveled and became empty, the nurse brought the remaining two bags. Their brownish-gold wrapping gave them a royal appearance, more prestigious than ordinary meds.

As she placed them down on a table, she yelled out again. This time, "Chemo check!"

The same nurse who had sprayed me with bio-freeze rushed over to ask, "What's your full name and date of birth?" When I told him, he clicked some keys to give his permission to proceed.

"For your first time," my nurse said, "we will infuse slowly to ensure you don't have an allergic reaction. If everything goes smoothly, we can speed up the process the next time you're here."

Once again, the medicine mixed with my blood, and luckily, I had no signs of an allergic reaction. As the liquid diminished, I wondered how soon the side effects would start.

"Time for lunch," my sister said after marking her page. "I'll head down to the cafeteria. What do you want to eat?"

I was hungry. "A turkey burger if they have it."

As Chris ventured downstairs with her wallet, leaving me alone with my thoughts, I couldn't help but feel disconnected from the patients around me. It was easy to relate to the French man. But by the look of everyone else, with gaunt faces and bald heads, I didn't want to accept that one day, soon, I might look like them.

With the takeout food containers covering the tray table, it was as if my sister and I were sitting down for a chemo room picnic. It was strange that no one else was eating lunch except for the French couple. When I took a bite, I was mentally prepared for the burger to taste like a mouthful of pennies since I'd heard that chemo can alter your tastebuds. But it tasted good. I savored it, unsure whether it would be the last good-tasting meal I'd have in a while.

"A pharmacist is on his way up to see you," the nurse told me and explained that I'd need to give myself a shot each day for the next five to keep my white blood cell count within range. I'd never given myself a shot before, or anyone else for that matter, but self-injecting sounded better than driving back and forth to the hospital on the usually-gridlocked 405 freeway to have a nurse do it for me.

Experiencing some fatigue after the third bag was depleted, I was glad when the pharmacist arrived at the beginning of the fourth. Wearing a white lab coat that wasn't buttoned, he tromped towards us, pulling an empty chair behind him. In his hands was a crumpled paper bag.

"You must take your medicine exactly twenty-four hours after you finish treatment," he said. "If you are done at three today, you must inject at three tomorrow." Releasing the bag from his grip, he pulled out an empty syringe. "This is a sample Zarxio shot. It must stay refrigerated and kept cold. When ready to use, pull it out of the fridge and give it thirty minutes to warm up to room temperature before injecting."

"Should we bring a cooler to keep it cold?" My chemo sidekick was all about logistics.

"That's a great idea," he said as I glanced around the room and noticed that no one else had an empty cooler sitting beside their feet. "Wash your hands and sterilize the area before touching the syringe. You need to avoid the risk of infection." Popping off the cap, he continued to explain while demonstrating. "Press the plunger down, s-l-o-w-l-y, allowing the air bubbles to surface at the tip of the needle." I had to use my imagination since there wasn't any liquid in the tube. "Release the bubbles before injecting." And then, I assume, imaginary bubbles were released.

He pulled out a piece of paper with step-by-step directions, which would be my self-injecting cheat sheet. My brain was running slow with only a quarter bag of chemo medicine remaining, so I was happy I didn't need to memorize everything.

He went on, "There are too many germs in the pharmacy, so you'll need to have the person who comes with you to treatment go down and pick up the prescription. You can no longer visit the pharmacy yourself."

The news woke me up. *Excuse me?* With everything going on that day, hearing that I'd have to rely on someone else to pick up my medicine made me feel as if my last shred of independence was being stripped away. I've always prided myself on self-sufficiency, and I suddenly felt helpless. Whether I liked it or not, my new way of life would force me to rely on others, which I considered a burden, not for me, but them.

By the time the pharmacist left, and before my sister could ask how I felt about everything, a tall, lanky woman took the pharmacist's seat, placing a satchel on the floor. Staring at me through thick glasses, she resembled the librarian in my elementary school with her maternal demeanor. Pulling out a small notebook, she prepared to take notes.

"I'm Debbie, the Oncology Social Worker. Where are you employed?" She held the pen to the paper, ready to record my response.

"I'm self-employed."

She scribbled down my answer. "So I assume you will not need a medical note written to an employer then?"

"That's correct." Being a freelancer and owning our own business has its drawbacks, especially the ups and downs of finances. But at that moment, I was happy about my career choice.

She reached into her bag and pulled out an "Advance Health Care Directive" to record my medical wishes and decisions in the event I could no longer decide for myself. But I wasn't sure why she chose to give me one at that moment. It felt like a premonition, curse, or both.

"Please take this home and fill it out. Bring it back the next time you have treatment. My business card is stapled to the front if you have any questions."

I have a question. Do you think I'm going to die? Because I've never fought harder to live than I am right now. And the paperwork you just handed me goes against everything that I am striving to do. But I didn't say any of that. Instead, I placed the "Directive" into my backpack and made a point of zipping the bag shut.

Debbie added, "It's National Cancer Survivors Day down in the courtyard." Her voice was filled with enthusiasm. "There are booths about wellness and healthy anti-cancer diets. We also have a panel of guest speakers who are survivors."

Now, *that* was perfect timing. Hearing that people were celebrating being cancer-free on the day of my first treatment felt like the Universe was sending me a message that the "Advance

Health Care Directive" was routine and not a foreshadowing of my fate.

Debbie looked over at my sister. "You should come downstairs with me and pick up some materials for Jennifer."

Chris shifted her body weight and looked uncomfortable. I could tell that she didn't want to leave my side. Lunch was one thing. Attending an event was another.

"You've been sitting all day," I told her. "It's good to move around. Go check it out!"

Chris said she'd pick up my Zarxio shots on her way back up and left with Debbie.

A few chairs over, a woman watched a talk show with a scarf wrapped around her head. Next to her, a man slept in a recliner, snoring like a bear. Destiny had booked us all a seat on Chemo Airlines, yet none of us knew if we'd make it to our destination. Instead of suffering upstairs, we all wanted to be down in the courtyard, celebrating with those who had safely returned to their regular lives.

My sister arrived with a white pharmacy bag and a huge grin. I knew that look; it was the expression she had right before expressing a witty comment or doing something funny.

"What is it?" I had to ask.

"I just walked through an inflatable colon! It's down there to educate people about colon cancer."

"A what?" Fatigued, I wanted to make sure I heard her correctly.

"A colon! It was as if I was a piece of poo traveling through it!" she said, which made us both crack up. For whatever reason, my sister always used the word "poo" when referring to poop.

Weighed down by all of our belongings, we blended into the festivities as we walked through the courtyard—and yes, past the giant inflatable colon—on our way to the parking garage. There was upbeat music and balloons tied to tents where vendors handed out free samples of healthy foods. T-shirts hung from racks that read TOUGHER THAN CANCER and WARRIOR.

That evening, I felt confident that the side effects might not be as bad as I had imagined. With only fatigue and no allergic reactions during the infusion, things were moving in the right direction. *One chemo down, five to go,* I thought. *Maybe chemo won't be so tough after all.*

WARRIOR SPIRIT

THE MORNING after my first chemo infusion, I went to the photo shoot and functioned at half-speed. My blood felt thick and heavy. Even with a good night's rest, I was exhausted. My mouth was dry and chalky, and when I yawned, it felt like my lips might crack. There was a delay and disconnect between my thoughts and speech, which was problematic as I needed to communicate efficiently for my job. Everything took extra energy that I didn't have.

When I opened the fridge to pull out the vinyl lunch bag containing my first immune-boosting shot, the smell of food made my stomach churn. I stashed the bag in the office and set the alarm on my phone to go off after half an hour once it warmed up to room temperature. When I returned to the studio floor, our client, Amanda, stood, confused, over a sea of colorful plates spread out on a table.

"Do you remember which recipe this is for?" she asked, holding up an oval plate.

Typically, I had an entire shoot list and every prop memorized, but at that moment, not a single thing came to mind. *This must be the chemo brain and cognitive fog Rhonda told me about.* Flustered but pretending everything was normal, I finally offered, "It went with the stir fry."

Is that right?

She raised an eyebrow, even more confused. "But we already shot the stir fry recipe. This plate is for something we haven't photographed yet."

"Let me check the shoot list," I said and rushed off. Rustling through papers, I frantically searched through notes struggling to comprehend them.

Our other client, Amanda's boss, finished a conference call and overheard the discussion. "It's for the chicken salad," she said as if it were the most obvious thing in the world.

When the alarm sounded on my cell phone, I was grateful to escape. I grabbed the vinyl bag and bolted to the single bathroom to wash my hands. I alcohol-swabbed my belly and popped open the needle cap, but when I pressed down on the syringe's plunger to release air bubbles, a missile of medicine arced through the air, landing on the back wall of the bathroom. *Oh no!* I checked the vial to see how much was left. Half was better than nothing.

With my left hand pinching my stomach fat and my right hand ready to insert the needle, I couldn't. *Don't overthink it. Just do it.* I still wavered. *You can do it.* Inhaling deeply, I finally forced myself to jab the needle into my abdomen. When I lifted my finger off the plunger to pull the needle out, it retracted into its casing just like it had done during the demonstration. I took another deep breath. *It's over. I did it.*

Ensuring nothing was left behind, I wiped down the streak of liquid on the wall with a paper towel and tossed the used alcohol swab and syringe packaging back into the vinyl bag. I looked around for telltale evidence. Anything left behind could poten-tially blow my I'm-perfectly-healthy-and-not-a-cancer-patient cover.

On the other side of the bathroom door, next to the kitchen, the food stylist asked the clients, "How would you like the grill marks shown on this piece of fish?"

As they bickered about char lines for a full five minutes, I couldn't help but think *how pointless to spend even one second worried about a piece of halibut. There are so many more important things to spend time doing.*

I hid in the office for the rest of the day. With every passing hour, my brain melted into sludge. Pain permeated my bones. My head throbbed and pulsated. My stomach twisted with knots. *Under these conditions, how will I ever be able to keep up this charade?*

When Bruce finally yelled, "It's a wrap," I was relieved I had made it through the day. Feeling worse by the minute, I needed to get home.

* * *

The side effects of the chemo and the Zarxio shots worsened throughout the week. Sitting up, lying down, or standing, I felt like I'd been hit by a bus. Food tasted like metal, which was ironically a positive. It curbed my appetite since eating made my stomach react like I had a slight case of food poisoning.

But life outside of cancer didn't stop. I still had to work, and every proposal took five times longer to complete. After triple-checking emails for errors, I'd still find missing words. When my professionalism suffered, so did my pride.

How will I get through this? I have to find a way.

I reminded myself of something important—life is full of patterns. An ocean that rises must fall. Hovering storm clouds always pass. After a forest fire, new growth begins. Identifying patterns of the side effects would allow me to plan my life accordingly and remind me that the pain and debilitation were only temporary.

On a paper calendar—*yes, old-school style*—I circled the date of my first chemo and then wrote down three simple questions. I'd document the answers daily.

1. How am I feeling overall? Ten was normal. One was awful. I jotted down "2" in the box.

2. What are the side effects? Headache, fatigue, chemo brain, nausea, stomach spasms, metallic-tasting food, zero appetite, bone and body aches, diarrhea, tingling in my fingers, pain in the balls of my feet.

3. How tired am I? Ten was rested. One was utterly exhausted. I was a "4."

If I can discover a pattern, it will guide me through the chaos.

* * *

Even though my eyes were heavy with sleep when the phone rang, I saw it was Utaiwan and picked up.

"How did your first chemo go?"

"It's a battle," was all I could say. I didn't have enough energy to elaborate.

"I won't keep you. Get some rest." And then she said, "You are my warrior, sweet tea," and hung up.

The 'warrior' label was kind but didn't sit well. Nothing about my sulking, depression, or misery made me feel like a 'warrior.' Warriors demonstrate great vigor and are strong mentally, emotionally, and physically. That wasn't me. I thought about the T-shirts displayed at National Cancer Survivors Day that read, WARRIOR. It was a common noun used to describe cancer patients, but I'd feel like a fraud if I bought one and put it on.

Needing to rest, I curled up on the sofa and turned on a documentary called *Free Solo*. In it, Alex Honnold, a professional rock climber, embarks on a dangerous journey to free-climb a cliff in Yosemite National Park. One poor grip or slipped step would result in Alex plummeting to his death. And yet, he chose to take that risk to prove that he could accomplish a feat few others would dare to try.

There's a scene in the documentary where Alex tells the viewers, "It's about being a warrior." *How ironic! There's that word,* I thought. "It doesn't matter about the cause necessarily. This is your path, and you'll pursue it with excellence. You face your fear because your goal demands it. That is the goddamn warrior spirit." I paused the film and replayed the scene. "It doesn't matter about the cause necessarily. This is your path, and you'll pursue it with excellence. You face your fear because your goal demands it. That is the goddamn warrior spirit."

Hearing it explained in that way, I grabbed my journal. Even with lingering chemo brain, there was a rush of clarity and inspiration.

And so I wrote:

LIFE IS FUELED BY AN INTERNAL FORCE, AND WHEN THREATENED, IT WILL RISE TO FIERCELY MEET ITS OPPONENT. A PERSON CANNOT BE LABELED A WARRIOR; THE SPIRIT INSIDE EACH OF US GRACIOUSLY TAKES ITS NAME.

The more I thought about the written words, the more I knew my warrior spirit was illuminated and ready to attack. The warrior spirit had nothing to do with my physical body, requiring no additional energy on my part. It was a force. One that lies deep within each of us, waiting to be called upon. And when needed, it rises up because our goal, *our life,* demands it.

Although I may not have felt like a 'warrior,' I knew deep down inside my warrior spirit was there, about to rise on my behalf.

CANCER CUTS DEEP

"What happened?" I asked when I opened the door to find Betty standing on our porch, pressing her shaking hand to her forehead, trying to keep blood from running into her eyes.

Without responding, she made a beeline to the kitchen with bloody droplets following her footsteps. Hovering over the sink, she splashed cold water on the cut as I handed her a clean cloth and grabbed a bag of ice from the freezer.

"Let me see," I said, prompting her to pull away the rag and reveal an inch-long gash above her left eyebrow.

Bruce walked into the kitchen, startled by the blood, his mom, a bag of ice, and me examining the wound. "Mom, what happened?"

"I fell on the curb outside," she said as she glanced at us from the corner of her eye.

"It's bad," Bruce told her. "We need to get you to the emergency room."

"Did you slip? How did this happen?" I asked again, still baffled.

"I wasn't thinking straight," she said, still hunched over the basin. And after a short pause, she asked, "How did your first chemo go?"

I couldn't believe it. Here she was, bleeding from a deep gash in her forehead, and yet, she was more worried about me and how the chemo went than her own injury.

"We have to go!" Bruce said with panic in his voice.

I agreed. Taking Bruce's lead, I rushed out of the kitchen to locate my shoes, keys, and purse. As I stumbled around trying to pull the back of my shoe on, Bruce led his mother to the door.

"Wait for me!" I said, trying to find the correct key to lock the house.

Bruce stopped, his arm latched onto his mother's, and said, "You can't go. There are too many germs."

"Oh, right," I said, remembering that avoiding high-risk places was one of the many rules of being a cancer patient.

The door shut. And from the protective bubble of safety inside our germ-free home, I watched his car back out of the driveway as it disappeared down the street without me.

As much as I pretended that *Feisty Righty* was no longer in control, it was. I had become a spectator of life. Even in an emergency, I was helpless and isolated.

Knowing that the realization might send me into a fit of depression, I told myself, "Stay positive and be productive." Essentially, stay busy.

The chemo calendar needed to be updated. I noticed a pattern had already formed. The further I got away from my first chemo, the better I started to feel. The side effects weren't gone, but they seemed a bit easier to tolerate.

Maybe I can still plan lunch dates with friends if my stomach continues to improve. When the chemo fog lifts, my work will become easier. I'll no longer feel lost in a sea of unknowns. And then, I suddenly saw a lighthouse, and that lighthouse was the life that I had always known and loved.

* * *

Three hours later, I heard the mechanical hum of the garage door and rushed to the living room to greet them. On Betty's head was a thick white bandage.

"How did it go?" I asked as she walked inside, this time without a trail of blood.

"They did a head scan," Bruce told me, "Everything checked out okay. She needed stitches but will have them removed in a week."

I turned to my mother-in-law to tell her how worried I was. She listened, but instead of elaborating on what had happened in the emergency room, she asked again, "How did your first chemo go?"

It made me laugh. "I think I am doing better than you are right now," I said, which made her laugh, too.

In bed that night, I couldn't stop thinking about her accident and the question that followed. Accidents happen, but given her unrelenting desire to find out about my chemo, I couldn't help but connect the two. Had she been so caught up in thinking about me that she didn't pay attention to where she was stepping? Was her mind consumed with worry, and that is why she wasn't thinking straight?

I thought to myself, *cancer cuts deep—not only for the patient but the caregivers—even without a fall.*

THE "ART OF LIVING"

When faced with a cancer diagnosis, or any potentially terminal disease, you evaluate your life microscopically. A million questions plague your mind about what you would have done differently and whether you've wasted any of the precious time you were given. Thinking back on practically every major decision I'd ever made helped me realize that the "art of living" differs from the "act of living."

The "act of living" is the physical aspect we all share. For example, eating, breathing, and sleeping represent the "act." But the "art of living" is how we make life uniquely ours. It's why we are born in the first place, and it creates the legacy we leave behind when we die.

Most of the time, it's easy to be caught up in the "act," the day-to-day tasks and routines that allow us to pay our bills, work harder to get the promotion, tote our children around to their numerous activities, and do it all over again the following day. There's nothing wrong with the "act" unless we have forgotten about the "art."

How often do we brush our talents aside? Or bury our

passions? Or not take a risk, even though we believe the outcome could result in pure, excited-to-be-alive joy? Why is it easier to become the person society wants us to be than show the world who we truly are? Is it in our best interest to avoid living the life we dream of?

But with a diagnosis, this type of self-evaluation—*or perhaps self-evolution*—occurs.

* * *

The phone rang, and it was the genetic counselor. "Good news," she said, "there are no gene mutations found in your blood work."

Relieved, I asked, "If it's not genetically linked, then what do you think may have caused the cancer?"

"In the medical world, we classify the cause as environmental."

"Like where I live or what I eat?" If something in my house had caused cancer, I was eager to get rid of it.

"Maybe. Any other questions?" I could tell she wasn't going to be forthcoming with answers. Once she knew I had no genetic link, her job was to move on and advise the patients that did.

When the call was over, I was at a loss. On one hand, I was glad it wasn't genetic and could proceed with the treatment plan I'd already started. But understanding why I got cancer was crucial for my healing. And without rooting out whatever carcinogens or threats were floating around in my environment, there was an increased chance of recurrence once I became cancer-free. Was I expected to purge everything in my home and start over? How could I? I didn't even know what to replace the old items with.

But then, in the midst of this confusion, a quote came to me. It was one said by Buddha. "What we think, we become." Essentially, how we navigate through the physical environment is largely influenced by introspection and our beliefs relating to that environment.

What happened in the nine months between my clear mammogram and finding the lump? How was I feeling? What consumed my thoughts? How was I handling stress? Was I depressed? In a state of self-neglect? The only way to move forward with a cancer-free future was to examine my cancer-causing past.

At my computer, I decided to identify the things about myself that needed improvement. What surprised me was that I already knew what they were, even though I had never outwardly acknowledged them before.

- BEING AN OVER-ACHIEVER (NEVER SATISFIED WITH WHERE I'M AT IN LIFE)
- A BELIEF THAT MATERIAL THINGS PROVIDE HAPPINESS (I NEEDED TO WORK HARDER TO OBTAIN MORE)
- BEING A CHRONIC WORRIER AND OVER-THINKER (FOCUSED ON WHAT MIGHT GO WRONG INSTEAD OF WHAT COULD GO RIGHT)
- PEOPLE PLEASER (PLACING MY HAPPINESS SECOND TO OTHERS')
- LACK OF BOUNDARIES (HARD TO SAY "NO" TO THINGS I DIDN'T WANT TO DO)
- FEELING STUCK IN LIFE, UNSATISFIED (IN SEARCH OF MY LIFE PURPOSE TO MAKE IT MORE MEANINGFUL)
- NOT LISTENING TO MY NEEDS
- AND, OF COURSE, LIFE'S SIMPLE LUXURIES HAD BEEN CAST ASIDE, AND I WAS THE ONE WHO HAD CHOSEN TO LET THEM GO.

* * *

As it turns out, I wasn't the only one carefully dissecting my life. Bruce's older brother called from Florida with his latest health update. Bruce motioned me over to listen.

"Brute," Bob always called Bruce, "my colon cancer has worsened. It hurts...," and then came a longwinded groan. "Feels like an ice pick is stabbing me. Man, I've lived a reckless life." He was referring to how he spent most of his adult years drinking heavily, smoking, partying, and crashing wherever he could. But now, instead of booze, he drank green vegetable smoothies hoping to counteract cancer without having to do chemotherapy. "But there may not be time left to change things," he added.

"What would you change?" Bruce asked.

"Let go of everything I thought was important, and instead, focus on everything that actually is," Bob replied as he groaned for the second time in pain.

Bob and I were both evaluating our lives simultaneously, 2,500 miles apart. He was analyzing his choices and whether he'd been too consumed with the "act of living" to focus on the meaning of life while I was busy struggling with my own realizations.

But then something life-altering happened. I realized that with every second, as long as we have another breath of life left inside of us, we are capable. Capable of positive change. Capable of living the life of our dreams. Capable of building a legacy for ourselves. Capable of making the world a better place. Capable of loving harder and living easier. Capable of embracing who we truly are.

It's not too late ... for me, for you, for Bob, for anyone. With every breath, there lies an incredible opportunity to breathe the "art" of life back into the "act." And if we do—*when we do*—our lives, *and us*, will flourish.

THE KID'S MENU

I SAT at the dining room table, trying to motivate myself to eat. Eating had become arduous in the days after my first chemo; nothing tasted the way it had before or was appetizing at all, and the smell of anything edible brought on waves of nausea. And yet, the doctors, nurses, and pamphlets encouraged me to eat as much as possible so I wouldn't drop weight too quickly.

You're down seven and a half pounds, I reminded myself as I lifted the spoon of mashed potatoes, took a bite, and then moved the mound of food around in my mouth before swallowing.

"Is it good?" Bruce asked as he devoured a cheeseburger.

Since he had made a special trip to get me takeout, I nodded with appreciation, swallowed, and then pulled my spoon back through the gravy, feeling pressure to take another bite, not because Bruce was watching, but because forcing myself to consume calories was at least one thing I still had control over.

During my first chemo, I overheard a patient talking to her nurse about how she could only eat rotisserie chicken. Breakfast, lunch, and dinner, all chicken, chicken, chicken.

"Every day?" the nurse asked.

"Every day. It's the one thing I found that works!" At the time, it seemed odd. I couldn't imagine wanting the same food even three days in a row, let alone every meal.

But now, it made sense. If chicken tasted good, and her digestive tract didn't revolt, then eating the same food, cooked the same exact way, was her only option. I had yet to discover my 'perfect food' because nothing in my vast repertoire of favorite foods sounded palatable.

I rested the spoon on top of the potatoes and watched as it slowly sank into the gravy. I felt guilty for not trying harder to make myself eat. *You can't stop now. Eat more. If you don't eat, you'll lose strength.*

I stared down into the bowl of potatoes as if I had watched someone lace them with poison. My belly was already spasming from the first few bites and I knew what would soon follow: diarrhea. Not just once or twice, but several episodes until I felt so depleted that I'd fall into bed, exhausted and hating mashed potatoes for the rest of my life. And so I forced one more bite and scooped the rest into a storage container. Even though I knew I'd never eat it, I placed it in the fridge anyway.

Unsure of how to manage food consumption for five more chemotherapy sessions, I called Aunt Marilyn, Don's wife, for advice. She was there when Don went through his treatment, and I knew she could provide insight.

After she asked several questions about how I was feeling, I then asked her, "Did Don have a problem eating while he was doing chemo?"

"Absolutely. He'd search all day for the one thing he could eat. When he told me what it was, no matter what, I'd figure out how to make it for him."

It was too familiar. Bruce had asked me earlier what I wanted for dinner, and when I said mashed potatoes, just like Marilyn, he went out to buy some.

"Not only does food taste weird," I told her, "but the smell is nauseating. Every smell is intensified."

She laughed. "Oh, I know. Donald was feeling good one day, so I invited him to join my friend and me for dinner. But when the food arrived, he wouldn't touch it. I wondered why. On our drive home, he asked me why Becky's perfume smelled so bad. I told him it smelled wonderful, like gardenias. But at that moment, I realized that what smelled good to me no longer smelled good to him—at least not while chemo was running through his system."

Her story reminded me of how much I now despised the smell of laundry detergent, candles, or anything infused with fragrance, which, these days, felt like pretty much everything.

"Are you eating?" she asked with concern.

"Yes, but like a five-year-old," I told her. "I'm now a macaroni and cheese, applesauce, peanut butter, pudding, and chicken tenders type of girl. Basically, anything you'd order off the kid's menu."

Her response was a chuckle. "Donald loved his vanilla ice cream. Chemo turned him into a five-year-old, too."

"So I'm not the only adult sitting at the children's table?" I joked.

"Nope. Definitely not. He would have been right there with you."

When we hung up, I thought about how often, pre-cancer, I'd put pressure on myself to stop eating. I'd feel guilty if I indulged in desserts around swimsuit season. Now post-cancer, I felt the same pressure and guilt. But this time, with the "Chemo Diet," I felt guilty for not eating enough.

My mind searched for a solution, and I thought about the calendar of side effects I'd created. Maybe in the week right before my next treatment, food would start to taste good again, and then I'd gorge on high-calorie foods to make up for the weight loss. Maybe I still just needed to find my 'rotisserie chicken dream food' that I knew I could count on to be appetizing when nothing else was. Maybe I'm just being weak. Other cancer patients experienced the same aversion to food, yet many of them keep their weight up.

I decided at that moment to change my tactics and listen to my body instead of my mind. I'd do my best to figure out the one food I craved each day and then try to eat, but if I couldn't, I would give myself permission to stop eating. While it was important to curb the weight loss, it was just as important to minimize the pressure and guilt, and resentment. Even though my shorts were already beginning to slip down around my hips and my shirts hung a little looser, I decided it was okay. When I began to feel better—further away from each treatment—I'd figure out how to gain some weight back. Maybe I'd actually feel hungry. And more than likely, with a hearty appetite, I'd probably order something off the kid's menu.

MEDIA MADNESS

Trying to calm the acid reflux caused by a few bites of mashed potatoes, I climbed into bed and turned on the television. The channel landed on a talent show competition where a young man in his twenties was being interviewed.

"My mom always encouraged me to pursue music," he said. "Three years ago, she was diagnosed with breast cancer." I perked up. "She went through conventional treatment and fought it." Now I was captivated. I hoped they'd cut to a woman in the audience with a smile on her face, clapping for her son, happy and excited to be a part of his moment. "But then it returned," he said, "and it was more aggressive the second time around."

My heart skipped a beat as I reached for the remote to quickly turn the channel. I didn't like where the interview was headed. All I could think about was *even when she won the battle against cancer, she couldn't win the war.*

Where is the remote? Searching for it in the folds of the comforter, listening to him talk about how proud she would have been, I became frantic. *Where is it?!* I needed to change channels before he announced that his mother had died from the same disease I was trying to fight.

"She told me in hospice she was never coming home."

Hearing those words, I stopped searching and looked back at the screen. It was too late. I'd heard it. She never came home. My eyes stung with tears, as did his. His sadness took hold somewhere on a sound stage surrounded by hot lights. Miles away in my bedroom, all alone, I cried with him, for his mother, and myself.

I had to take my mind off the musician's tragic story, so I figured social media might lighten the depressing mood. As I scrolled past online pictures of cute babies, vacation photos, and a friend's recently remodeled kitchen, I landed on a page about organic living. Hoping for some light-hearted innocuous post like a couscous recipe or advice on growing the perfect tomato, there was an article titled "The Evils of Chemotherapy."

Ignore it. Don't click on it. But I clicked.

Expecting the worse, I was surprised that there wasn't anything in the article that I didn't already know. Yes, chemo impacts the entire body. Yes, chemo attacks healthy cells as well as rogue ones. Yes, it can cause permanent damage to organs long after cancer has been beaten into submission. I thought that with "evil" in the title, there might be some new side effects I wasn't aware of.

What I wasn't prepared for were the comments that followed. Of course, some people were positive and supportive, but others were, well, despicable.

The worst ones read:

PAIGE C.: ANYONE WHO CHOOSES CHEMO IS STUPID BECAUSE IT'S A DEATH SENTENCE.

NICKI G: IF YOU HAVE CANCER, YOU'RE GOING TO DIE ANYWAY. WHY BOTHER?

OMAR S.: CHEMO KILLS HUMANS, NOT CELLS.

I felt personally attacked. *Don't they understand that a cancer patient might be reading their comments? Do they even care?* If chemotherapy could be labeled as evil, then some of these people, cloaked in the anonymity of their avatars and screen names, were ten times more wicked.

Pre-cancer, I would have ignored them. But being emotionally unstable, terribly tired, and barely coping, I couldn't shake it. Out of disbelief, I was drawn to read more.

LINSEY D.: PEOPLE WHO GET CANCER DESERVE IT. THEY SHOULD HAVE TAKEN BETTER CARE OF THEMSELVES.

Stop reading.

DANNY P.: CHEMOTHERAPY KILLED MY BROTHER.

Okay, that's enough. I logged off.

But over the next hour, their words played over and over again in my mind. And when doubt crept in, I remembered what Grandpa Wells had told my mom, "Don't judge a person until you've walked three days in his shoes."

It works both ways, right?

As I thought about their nasty, unhelpful remarks, I noted the hostility and rage. Rage toward the disease, rage toward those affected, and rage toward a treatment that didn't work. The *Five Stages of Grief,* according to Elisabeth Kubler-Ross, are: denial, anger, bargaining, depression, and acceptance. It was evident that many of these people had lost someone close and couldn't get past the second stage.

Perhaps they lashed out online because there was no other outlet. Perhaps they weren't so different than the young man in the talent competition who wished his mother was still alive. Perhaps animosity was the only way they knew how to cope or convince themselves they were moving forward. Maybe if they blamed chemotherapy, then just maybe, for a few minutes, they'd have something tangible to blame for stealing away someone they loved.

Regardless, that night, something became apparent. My world had shifted from one without cancer to one infiltrated by it. I cried with a stranger on television. Hair commercials now triggered jealousy. Comments on social media made me question my intuition. Even if I wanted to remain in my old life, there was no way I could. I had changed. The cancer had changed me, and there was no going back.

WISDOM

"You have hair?!" Dr. Santos said in shock when he walked into the exam room for a follow-up two weeks after my first chemo.

"Yes!" I said proudly.

I'd worked hard to keep it as long as I could, even holding it back when people hugged me so it wouldn't be pulled out by accident. I rarely brushed or even touched it. Every saved strand was an accomplishment. The longer it stayed on my head, the longer my secret lived.

"But losing your hair is a good thing," he informed me, worried. "It means the chemo is working."

I hadn't considered that becoming bald showed my oncologist that his chemo treatment plan was working. By the looks of me and my hair, the chemo wasn't successfully doing its job.

Washing his hands, he asked, "Have you felt the tumor lately?"

"No way!" I said, sitting back. Sure, I had looked at my breast in the shower after my targeted mammogram, and even then, with all the bruising, it felt like a huge mistake. The thought of actually feeling "it" again made me cringe.

"You should," he said, taking a seat on a stool as he pressed firmly into my breast with his fingertips. I quietly stared across the room at an illustration of a human body that hung on the wall. "This is good! The mass is smaller and softer. After only one treatment, this is incredible! Imagine how it'll be after five more." I could tell he was proud of himself for choosing an effective chemo cocktail and that he loved shutting cancer down as much as I loved he was doing it.

"That's amazing," I told him, feeling an abundance of gratitude.

After he documented my hefty list of side effects and asked if I had any questions, it was time for him to see another patient. On his way out of the room, he stopped.

"The next time I see you," he remarked, pointing his finger at me, "I hope you don't have hair."

He was dead serious.

I smiled. As much as he *wanted* my hair gone, I *needed* my hair to keep my secret alive. Besides, the tumor shrunk, isn't that proof enough?

Stuck in traffic, I sought out shortcuts on my way to Beverly Hills for my scheduled breast MRI. When I found the building, I sped down to the basement, parked, and jogged to the elevators. When the doors opened on the ground level, I was relieved to find the imaging center's entrance directly in front of me.

After completing the forms given to me by the receptionist, I sat in the waiting room wondering what to expect. I had never had an MRI before, and when I asked THE SECRET SOCIETY about it, I received several warnings:

"The machine is loud; you may need earplugs."

"It's tough to hold still for that long."

"Have your doctor prescribe anti-anxiety medicine. It is the only way to get through it."

Chris, who had torn ligaments in both knees and had undergone multiple MRIs, advised me to convince myself I was in a tanning bed. "If you start to feel like you're going to panic, just close your eyes and imagine you're lying on a beach with nothing but expansive blue sky above you." It sounded good until she followed it up with, "And don't open your eyes."

Nervous or not, I was determined to cross another thing off the "to-do" list. Besides that, the MRI would confirm the tumor's size and pinpoint the location. It would also reaffirm (hopefully) that there wasn't any cancer in Lefty and bring me closer to finding out if they could identify disease in my lymph nodes.

A nurse called my name and walked me back to a changing room, where I soon realized that even in one of the wealthiest neighborhoods in the country, all medical gowns looked and smelled the same.

"When was the last time you had bloodwork done?" she yelled through the curtain between us.

"A couple of weeks ago, before my first chemo!" I shouted back. When dressed, I opened the curtain to find the nurse standing there with an annoyed look on her face and her hands planted on her hips.

She huffed, "Dr. Hu was supposed to send the results over. She didn't."

I reminded myself ... *she's on TEAM JENNIFER. She's here to assist. Be nice.*

"It seems unusual that she sent me here and didn't send what you needed. Are you sure you don't have a copy?" I trusted Dr. Hu, who seemed much more professional than the agitated nurse.

Race-walking down the hallway, she lectured, "We must ensure your kidneys and creatine levels are strong enough to handle the contrast dye. Without a copy of your recent blood-work, it's a problem."

"Is there a way to contact Dr. Hu's office to get it?" I was desperate for a solution.

"I have a Plan B," she announced as we veered in a different direction to a room where a young nurse sat at a desk with her back to us. The angry nurse cleared her throat loudly to get her attention.

"What?" she responded, completely irritated.

"Melinda, take this woman's blood."

As she rushed out, Melinda told me to take a seat. A minute or so later, she got up out of her chair and walked over. She looked to be in her mid-twenties, although it was hard to tell under her smeared mascara and eyeliner.

"Place your arm on the table," she said and then tapped my forearm with her perfectly manicured nails. After flicking my skin several times, she dropped her head in what seemed like defeat. *Is she that upset she can't find a vein?* "I'm sorry," she admitted, "but I am feeling off today. At lunch, I had a big fight with my boyfriend." *This is uncomfortable.* She must've noticed my unsettled expression because she quickly changed the subject. "What type of MRI are you getting done?"

"Breast. I was diagnosed with breast cancer fifty-one days ago, and fifteen days ago, I had my first round of chemotherapy."

"Did they find cancer during a mammogram?" She resumed the tapping and flicking of my forearm.

"I found it myself. By accident."

"That's so scary. What did you do when you were diagnosed with cancer?"

"I was in shock at first until the news sank in." A tear dribbled off her cheek when I looked up at her face.

Is she crying? Crying about my story? My cancer? Or had she drifted back to the worst lunch date of her life? More of her mascara slid down her face with the loose tear.

Still searching for a viable vein, she picked up a boxy device and moved it over my arm as if scanning sand with a miniature metal detector. "With everything you've been through," she said, "you must have a unique perspective on life."

I couldn't help but think about how much I had changed. "Yes, it certainly provides a unique perspective."

"I'd love to get your advice." *Oh no.* "I'm sure you have so much wisdom. More than the rest of us." *Do I?* Before I could respond, she launched into her story. "I've been with Thomas for two years now. We have fun together, but he doesn't take our relationship seriously." Satisfied that she had found a vein, she pierced my skin with a needle and, realizing she had *not* found a vein, quickly pulled it back out. Grabbing a tissue from a box, she started to dab up the blood. "He likes to party. Too much. I am not looking to party for the rest of my life." *Does she even know how to draw blood? Please tell me this isn't her first time.* "What do you think?" she asked. *I think you should focus on your job. Find a good vein. Get me out of here.* It now made sense why the bold-faced nurse called her a 'Plan B,' and it seemed that the 'B' stood for 'BAD.'

At the same time, I could feel this woman's struggle. Being an empath, a fixer, and a pleaser, I felt obligated to say something to help.

"Are you looking to settle down?" I asked, staring at the tissue now soaked with bright red dots of blood.

"I am!" She looked surprised, as if I had some unique psychic ability. She was desperate for me to be an all-knowing-cancer-patient guru.

"Are you looking to get married one day?" I asked.

"You get me!"

With one of my blue veins bulging, she inserted the needle

again. It hurt. I rarely feel pain when someone draws blood, but then again, an experienced and focused phlebotomist usually does it. I clenched my jaw to see if she'd notice, but she didn't.

"We argue a lot. He tells me I need to relax. What do you think I should do?" *Find a new career path. Get a different boyfriend. Pull yourself together.* But I knew from her internal sadness that Melinda needed sound advice instead of being judged. If I could give her a different outlook, maybe I could help.

I rattled off, "Don't force yourself to fix something broken. If you're supposed to be with him, it'll work out. Sometimes it is easy to overthink things, but usually, the answer is right in front of you."

"I like that," she remarked. I could see she was genuinely taking in what I had said by how her eyes widened, exposing more smudges of eyeliner beneath her lower eyelids.

Maybe I AM an all-knowing-cancer-patient guru, I thought.

Another nurse wandered into the room, searching for a manilla file folder. As she shuffled through a stack of papers, it was easy to notice that she wore a wig. No matter how she crouched or moved, the hair stayed in place. She hurried out, holding up a folder to let us know she found what she needed.

Melinda moved in closer. "Denise is a breast cancer survivor."

"That's fantastic!" I said, thrilled.

"I'm not sure if you noticed," she whispered, "but she wears a wig. Her hair never grew back after chemo." As soon as she said it, fear struck me like lightning. *Why did she say that? Why would she tell me that?*

I turned around to see the stern nurse had re-entered the room. "Stop what you're doing," she told Melinda. "I found the test results." *Did I go through all of this for nothing?* "Take her back to the MRI room."

Melinda did as she was told. With my arms covered in multiple band-aids, we strolled down the hallway toward an open door. The slow pace of her walk confirmed that our conversation hadn't ended.

"So, I should just let things play out with Thomas?" she concluded.

"I think so. See what happens."

We stopped in front of a room. I could see two MRI technologists patiently waiting inside. "Do you think we should break up?" There was a note of desperation in Melinda's voice.

"Trust your gut," I told her, displaying the wisdom of an all-knowing-cancer-patient guru. "It never steers you wrong. I think you already know what's best."

Before passing me off, she acted like she wanted to hug me but realized it would be inappropriate. "Thank God I met you today," she said.

God works in mysterious ways.

Inside the room, on a bed, I was told to lie face down. My breasts dangled through an opening. With my arms extended out like Superwoman in flight, the other employee placed a widget in my hand with a large round button on it.

"If you need us to stop the MRI at any point, press the button. But please know, you'll have to come back another time and start over," the technologist informed me. *There is no way in hell I am pressing that button.*

The bed retracted into a tunnel, and the machine started up like a clunky old car engine. My right arm fell asleep from holding its position. I imagined an expansive blue sky. *I am lying on the beach in Aruba,* I thought. My sister was right; it worked.

I saw Denise, again, out in the hallway afterward. She smiled at me, which outshined the perfect, artificial-looking wig that topped her head. I couldn't help but smile back. Even without having her natural hair, she seemed okay. Even happy.

And then it hit me. Like a wise all-knowing-cancer-patient guru once told Melinda, "Sometimes it is easy to overthink things, but usually the answer is right in front of you." I had been so concerned about losing my hair and the idea of it never growing back that I had forgotten the most important thing of all. Hair or no hair, Denise was grateful to be alive. And if that situation should happen to me, I only hoped my smile would shine as brightly as hers. If we're lucky, life goes on.

And the most important thing is: always go along with it.

UNPRECEDENTED LOVE

Seventy-nine days since I discovered the lump, 21 days after my first chemotherapy, and within an hour of going to the oncology department for my second chemo infusion, my mom passed by the bathroom where I was getting ready.

She glanced in to see my wet hair and asked, "Do you need to use the hair dryer? I can give you mine since the guest bathroom doesn't have one."

"No way!" I responded. "A single puff of air from the hair dryer might blow the remaining strands out of my head." It sounded like a joke, but we both knew it wasn't, which made us laugh hysterically.

Yes, it was *that* fragile.

To the point that I had modified my usual hair-washing method from massaging my scalp to placing shampoo in the palm of my hand and gently dabbing my hair with it. When it came to rinsing the shampoo out, I never ran my fingers through it. Instead, I'd let the water from the showerhead cascade over it. *Dab-and-rinse* was the only way to protect it.

With every passing day, I was growing concerned by the patches of missing hair. It wasn't enough loss to wear a ball cap, but it still required intentional styling to cover up the missing chunks. When a tiny knot of hair formed by my ear that morning, I tried to untangle it with a comb. But instead of the knot untangling, the comb pulled the loose clump out of my scalp without any pain or effort. I placed the dead hair into the trash can and set an empty toilet paper roll over the top to hide it.

The thought, "*Soon I'll be cancer-patient bald,*" was interrupted by my sister's text.

CHRIS: I'M OUT FRONT.

* * *

Walking into the chemo room for my second cocktail infusion felt different. I no longer needed to acclimate. Everything was now familiar. I looked around for the French man, but he wasn't there, which meant his schedule was now different than mine.

I settled into the recliner and made a silent dedication to my Grandma Wells. *This one is for you. It may not be as bad as a bone marrow test, but I'm guessing it's a close second.* My love and adoration for her would channel the courage I needed to forge ahead.

Since my body had tolerated the first treatment without any allergic reactions, the nurse increased the flow of the drip, which shortened my infusion time. Saving an hour and a half allowed us to go out for lunch at a restaurant instead of having a chemo room picnic. Thanks to my calendar documenting the side effects and with my stomach feeling stronger, I knew I had 18 hours left to enjoy the taste of food and consume calories before the "Chemo Diet" set in.

As we sat in a booth at the restaurant, finishing our late lunches and splitting a brownie, I realized that the brownie wasn't the only treat. Time with my sister was a rare treat, too.

"So tell me, do you really think the blue bridesmaid dresses will look better than the yellow ones?"

"Absolutely. You must go with blue," I told her, rehashing an earlier conversation we had during chemo. I had successfully argued that the blue dresses would look better with the diverse skin tones of her bridesmaids, and I'm sure they would have thanked me.

"Just think," my sister told me, her teeth coated in a thick layer of chocolate frosting, "you only have four treatments left."

I smiled back with chocolate coating mine. "I can't wait for it to be over with."

"You'll be finished with all of this soon," she said, washing the brownie bite down with a swig of iced tea.

I soon discovered that chemo accumulates in your system, making the side effects for the second round more acute than the first. Struggling and in pain, I thought, *how can I possibly get through the third, fourth, fifth, and sixth if I feel worse each time around?*

Three days later, after my lunchtime nap on the sofa—which was one of the many ways I figured out how to have enough energy to keep working—I opened my eyes and experienced a searing pain throughout my entire body. Like the kitten, Survivor, I cried out in hopes Bruce might hear me.

Bruce rushed in to sit next to me on the sofa. We just sat there, quiet, as the dappled afternoon light danced on the wall from the window. Eventually, without a word, Bruce picked up my hand and massaged my palm. I looked at his wedding band of 12 years, soon to be 13, wrapped around his finger. After all this time together, my diagnosis had turned Bruce into a nurturer.

Don't get me wrong; he has always been a loving and

supportive partner. At midnight, he'd run to the pharmacy to fix my cough. He helped me in and out of bed when I injured my back. But now, it was different. Although tasked with a job he never applied for, he was acing it.

Being a caregiver isn't easy, I thought.

Bruce no longer played golf with his buddies but didn't complain. Although we watched TV instead of going out for dinner and drinks, he never mentioned how he felt about staying home. Even though friends still called us to socialize when they visited Palm Springs, we didn't go, even though I am sure he wished that we could. He had put his life on hold, too.

I placed my head on his shoulder, and all I could say was, "I'm sorry."

"There's nothing to be sorry about," he replied.

"But I am. I am sorry for putting you through all of this."

Surrounded by framed photos, it was impossible not to notice how happy we were before my diagnosis. Happy in Paris. Happy in Peru. Happy in our family picture with Stella. Without the photos, I wasn't sure if I'd be able to remember what our lives were once like. But staring back at us, in all of them, we were so *very* happy.

"I just wish I could do more to help you," he said, "but I have no idea what to do."

"I have no idea either. We just... keep going," I said, encouraging him and myself to stay positive. By the look on his face, I knew he needed more from me.

Throughout our marriage, we'd never had a problem discussing challenging issues like finances and whether we should have children. But his role as a caregiver and mine as a patient was a discussion we hadn't had. It was long overdue.

And so I said, "I love having you share the same space with me, even if we're watching something on television. But at times, as you know, I like that you give me space, too. Empathy is great. I appreciate that you try to understand what I am going through but never feel sorry for me. I don't like pity."

"Is there anything I shouldn't say?"

"It's best to avoid certain phrases as a way to comfort me."

"Like what?"

"It's hard to hear the phrase, "Things could be worse," or, "You've got this." It makes me feel as if my concerns are disregarded. It's okay if you don't know what to say. Showing me love is enough. Taking me to a medical appointment speaks volumes. Massaging my hand when my body hurts does wonders," I said and then smiled, looking down at his hand with mine.

"I wonder...," he said and then stopped.

"You wonder what?"

"How do you have the strength to keep fighting?"

And then, without any hesitation, out came, "I fight to have more moments with the people I love."

This was a pinnacle moment of my journey. Until then, I wanted to live longer for myself. I wanted to cross things off my bucket list, which consisted mostly of activities like traveling to Greece, riding in a hot air balloon, or doing something trivial like goat yoga. But my motivation had changed. The journey was no longer about me but about them. I'd endure every prick, poke, and treatment to make more memories with my loved ones.

And then a feeling of euphoria ran through me. I was captivated by this deep-rooted, intense level of love that I had never experienced before. Without accurate words to describe it, I would say it felt as if I was *standing in the presence of God*, as the feeling enveloped my being. I could feel the love of our ancestors and their ancestors, crossing dimensions of time, and the love was undeniable, invincible, and nothing but pure joy.

I sat there, shocked and amazed. Although I always knew

what love felt like, never before had love felt quite like this. And maybe wanting to spend more time with loved ones can be viewed as slightly selfish, but what matters in life is the "we." That day, the "me" dropped from the equation, leaving nothing behind but life-altering unprecedented love. I'd endure anything for "them."

A CAREGIVER'S GUILT

AFTER EXPERIENCING UNPRECEDENTED LOVE, I was stumped about what I should buy Bruce for our anniversary. Ordinary presents like a home-brewing beer kit or monogrammed slippers seemed substandard. But with only two days left before our 13th anniversary, I had to figure something out. Quick.

Several dead-end online searches later, the phone rang. "I have some promising news about your breast MRI results," Dr. Hu shared. "There isn't any cancer in your left breast."

"That's incredible!" It confirmed the accuracy of the ultrasound. "What about my lymph nodes?"

I'd never thought much about the small, kidney-shaped glands in my armpits until my diagnosis. But when you get cancer, you quickly learn the importance of lymph nodes. Their status had become an obsession.

"It appears the cancer is contained within the tumor, but we will know more after surgery," it was the same thing she had told me before. "But I did notice that the tumor is much larger than we originally thought," she added, which was something new and devastating.

My heart skipped a few beats. *How can that be? Dr. Santos confirmed that Feisty Righty is now smaller and softer after my first chemo. How big was the tumor to begin with?*

"It's not unusual to see tumors larger than expected after reviewing the results of an MRI," she explained. "And I did have the opportunity to speak with Dr. Santos. He confirmed the chemo is working, which is excellent news. But he did want me to pass along something."

"Oh yeah, what's that?"

"He wanted me to tell you that you better be bald the next time he sees you," she conveyed, which made us both laugh.

"Of course he did," I replied.

After we hung up, in order to distract myself from thinking about my SUPER-SIZED tumor, I went back to hunting for a gift and scrolled past more unimportant items like a personalized whiskey barrel and a pair of glass lovebirds. *Stuff doesn't matter; moments do.*

I wanted to give Bruce a special moment. *But what? What does he need more than anything?*

And then I said out loud, "He needs an escape from me."

It was the unfortunate truth, and I knew what I needed to do. *A spa day!* And so, I booked three back-to-back appointments at a nearby resort with access to a saltwater pool, sauna, relaxation room, and jacuzzi. It would be the perfect gift.

On the morning of our thirteenth anniversary, as soon as the sunlight spilled into our bedroom, I placed a small box containing the spa voucher on Bruce's belly, hoping the weight of it would wake him up. I waited and waited as it rose and fell with each breath. I finally tapped his leg with my toes. He opened his eyes to see me staring at him with a giant smile.

"What's going on?" he asked, wanting to roll over to go back to sleep. When he went to pull up the blanket to his chin, his hand found the present. "What's this?"

I couldn't contain myself. "Happy Anniversary, baby!"

He sat up, put on his reading glasses, and carefully unwrapped the box. Pulling out the voucher, he read it quietly to himself as I thought, *I can't wait for him to tell me how much he loves it.* But he just sat there, holding the sheet of paper, staring down at it.

"It's a spa day!" I told him, hoping to help him understand what a fantastic gift it was. By his pensive reaction, I wondered if I should have settled on the monogrammed slippers or whiskey barrel.

"Yes, I know," he told me.

"Well, do you like it?" I asked, trying to hide my disappointment and still hoping his lack of enthusiasm had more to do with being tired than the gift.

"Honestly," he finally said, "I feel guilty going without you."

"Don't feel bad. I want you to go."

"But you'll be home by yourself on our anniversary. That doesn't seem right. What will you do while I'm away?"

"I'll be okay," I assured him. "You deserve this." I hated that my disease created such a sense of responsibility that he felt guilty if he did something nice for himself.

"Are you sure about this?" he asked.

"I'm positive. I'll drive you there. Take your time and enjoy it. When you're finished, text me, and I'll come by and pick you up. We can get takeout on our way home."

And there it was, the smile I had been waiting for.

He jumped out of bed, grabbed his backpack, and filled it with a change of clothing, a pair of sandals, and his swim trunks. While he was getting ready, I put on my ball cap to wear in front of him for the first time.

"Cute cap!" *He noticed.*

Little did he know it was about to become my identity. My crutch, always worn in public. Most of the photographs taken in the thirteenth year of our marriage would show me wearing it. It was the "black cap" era of our lives.

When I picked him up from the spa several hours later, with his face rosy and refreshed, I asked, "How was it?"

"Perfect," he said, throwing his backpack in the backseat and getting in. "I needed that."

As we pulled away, I looked over at him and said, "I want you to start hanging out with your friends again. Being a caregiver is tough. You deserve breaks from time to time."

"We'll see," he said with a shrug.

And he never talked about the subject again.

MY INDEPENDENCE DAY

THE FOURTH of July was red, white, and a depressing kind of blue.

Independence Day has always been one of my favorite holidays, but in 2017, the Fourth of July fell one week after my second chemo treatment, and I was in no mood to enjoy it. Normally we'd spend the day at Chris and David's house, eating chicken wings and ribs, drinking beer, and eventually walking down to the beach to watch the fireworks display. Since my immune system was compromised and my stomach was a mess, we opted for a less lively night at home, away from people. Bruce had suggested that we order some barbecue takeout, but I didn't have an appetite, so he settled on whatever leftovers were still in the fridge.

While it felt like everyone else in the country was celebrating, I was physically ill. And now, with a new side effect, hot flashes (which only made the heat of the Palm Springs summer feel even hotter), I was still stuck between a pre-cancer and post-cancer world. Feeling resentful, I cried. I looked at everything other people seemed to take for granted, like having a picnic, floating on the lake in inner tubes, or hanging out with friends, as unfair. *I've already got cancer. Can't I enjoy a holiday?* Although no one ever claimed that life *was* fair, it felt like mine had hit an all-time low.

I spent most of the day in bed while Bruce labored out in our front yard planting cacti. Occasionally, I'd glance out the bedroom window to check on him. He carefully transferred each cactus from their plastic pots into the ground and packed dirt around them, hoping they'd grow.

A little girl on her bike fiercely pedaled down the sidewalk to keep up with her older brother, the pink streamers from her handlebars trailing behind. Fireworks in the neighborhood went off with sharp snaps and sizzles. Even indoors, I could smell the sulfur from the mini-explosions. The neighbors felt like celebrating. I didn't. And that fact made me even more depressed.

As the unforgiving heat finally began to wane and the sun began to set, with my face planted in my pillow, I heard a tapping on the window. I didn't want to look over and make eye contact with Bruce since my eyes were red from hours of crying. He kept tapping and tapping on the pane, so with no other choice, I turned to see him standing there, motioning for me to come outside. I knew he wouldn't stop tapping until I got out of bed, so I did.

When I stepped outside, he was waiting for me. "Go take a seat," he said.

He hurried into the garage as I walked over to one of our patio chairs. I waited, listening to "God Bless America" piped over someone's outdoor speaker. Occasionally, I'd hear some random voices singing along as I thought, *I just want to go back to bed.*

Finally, Bruce came out of the garage with three long narrow boxes tucked under his arm and an orange utility bucket, which sloshed water with every step. As he got closer, I could see the picture on the boxes—sparklers.

He tore open one of the boxes, pulled out a stick, and searched his pocket for a lighter. Igniting it, he waited until it started shooting metallic sparks and handed it to me. *I haven't held a sparkler in years.* I could feel its electrifying energy as I watched the tiny pops and sparks. It had a life force of its own, cracking and sputtering and emitting a bright, brilliant light. Despite the neuropathy in my fingers and aches in my arms, I was suddenly compelled to wave the sparkler around.

I was mesmerized by the glowing tip, which emitted thousands of tiny stars in various blue, orange, and yellow hues. Bursting into the air, they glowed with incredible intensity before fading into the night.

"What do you think?" Bruce asked, excited.

"It's beautiful," I said. "I love this."

I stood up and twirled the sparkler around, watching the tracers. As soon as a sparkler burned out, Bruce replaced it. With sparklers in each hand, I drew cosmic wings, big and bright, on each side of me.

I felt alive.

By the third box, I wanted to dance. Shuffling my feet back and forth, I no longer cared about my broken body. I danced to the sounds of normalcy all around us: people talking down the street, kids splashing in their swimming pool next door, and an occasional passing car blasting music. By the time the last sparkler burned out, I felt as if I had been reborn.

That night, when I crawled into bed, I reflected on those glorious cosmic wings I had painted, surrounding my body in trails of white. I knew it was time to let go of the pre-cancer past I'd been trying to hang onto and transcend into the new life I had yet to create. Two months and four days after my diagnosis, 29 days after my first chemotherapy, I was finally ready to shave my head and say goodbye to the scraps of dead hair. It was time to start fresh and create space for new growth and beginnings.

* * *

The following day, Bruce set up a makeshift barbershop in our backyard, complete with a folding chair, electric razor, broom, and the new dustpan I had bought at Target with my ball cap purchase.

"How should I go about doing this?" Bruce asked nervously as he stood over me with a buzzing razor.

"Do whatever it is that works best."

"Should I work in rows as if mowing the lawn?"

"Sure." *Rows, diagonals, chevron patterns. It doesn't matter. I need it all off.*

He started at the nape of my neck. As Bruce slid the razor over the left side of my scalp toward my ear, the mechanical buzz grew louder. Several strands of hair landed on my lap. Opening my palms to catch some, I clenched a handful of scraps. Coarse and lifeless, the hair had died long before I was ready to part with it.

I started to feel a cooling sensation as more and more hair was removed. It was as if every hair follicle was exposed, and the action was breathing life back into them.

"I hope you like what I am doing." Bruce still seemed unsure of himself, but I knew he was doing the right thing.

"Remove every last strand," I assured him.

Stella's curiosity led her over to sniff at a clump of hair that had fallen near my feet. A few strands tickled her nose, and she let out a loud sneeze.

"I am going to remove the entire ponytail now," Bruce warned.

Closing my eyes, I imagined it to be the final tribute to the life I once had. The vibration of the razor hummed across the back of my neck, and I opened my eyes to find my dishwater-blonde ponytail still held together by a black hair tie on the ground.

Bruce placed the ponytail on Stella's head between her pointed ears. "It's her tiny toupee," he exclaimed. Stella shook it off. (Apparently, she doesn't like wigs, either.)

Once he was done, Bruce swept up the remaining clumps and placed them into the trash, which felt symbolic. I was ready for it to be hauled away. But when it came to the ponytail, I had second thoughts and couldn't discard it. I took it inside, tucked it into a cloth bag, and hid it in a drawer. I remembered what Rhonda said during my orientation to chemo, "I've heard some women keep a lock of their hair as a keepsake," which I thought was weird at the time, but now, like so many other things, it made sense. It's a beautiful and cherished souvenir of the life I once had.

I look at my pre-cancer past as the caterpillar years of my existence. Just as a caterpillar transforms, I knew, closing the drawer, what I needed to do. It was time to grow wings in hopes that I'd unfold them and fly free post-cancer.

SUNLIGHT

BEING NEWLY BALD REQUIRED A SELFIE. I texted the picture to my sister with my mouth ajar and my finger pointing to my baldness as if she wouldn't have noticed my new hairstyle, or lack of it, without the exaggerated pose.

Seconds after the text was sent, my sister called. "You did it!"

"I did!"

"How does it feel?"

"Liberating. I needed a fresh start," I told her, without going into detail about how I was motivated the night before by creating cosmic wings with sparklers.

"How are you holding up with the side effects?"

"I'm coping but worried about surviving the next four chemo treatments."

"But after the next one, you're already halfway through!" She announced with encouragement—the type of motivation that helped pull me through college at the mid-way point.

But this was bigger than getting through mid-terms or finals. I genuinely didn't know how to survive the next four treatments in my current physical state. *Will my heart stop? Will my lungs continue to breathe? Will I need to be hospitalized?* As much as I wanted to be strong, I questioned if my body was up for the task of surviving.

"Hey," she asked, "did you ever fill out the paperwork the social worker gave you?"

"The 'Advance Health Care Directive'?"

"Yeah."

"Not yet." *Dang, she remembered. (*But a good chemo sidekick never forgets.)

"I'll help you with it," she offered.

It didn't feel like the right time, but then again, it never would be. Reluctantly, I pulled the booklet from my backpack, grabbed a pen, and opened the document that would state my wishes regarding medical care at the end of my life.

I read the first question out loud, "Upon my death, would I like to donate my organs, tissue, and parts?"

"How do you feel about that?" Chris asked.

"If someone wants them, they can have them," I said, checking the YES box next to transplant, therapy, research, and education. "Do I wish to have cardiac resuscitation to try and prolong my life?" Another, YES.

"What's the next question?"

"Do I wish to have life support used to replace or support my natural breathing?"

"And?"

"Of course!" I checked the YES box. Considering that I not only had chemo brain but was doing everything in my power to live, I wondered if choosing YES to everything had more to do with my current drive than with rational thought. "Do I prefer to be buried or cremated?"

"What do you think?"

"I want to be cremated, with my ashes spread in Peru at Machu Picchu," I replied, not knowing if there were restrictions about ash spreading inside an Incan citadel or if my sister would even be allowed to bring my ashes to South America by plane.

"Mark it down," my sister said, although I sensed the uncertainty in her voice.

"Who would I like to attend my funeral?"

"Would you like a large gathering or keep it small?" she asked.

"Invite THE SECRET SOCIETY," I told her, shortening the guest list.

After grudgingly answering a few more questions, I landed on the finale. "Which song would I like played at my funeral?" An absurd question deserved a ridiculous response. "How about 'Stayin' Alive' by The Bee Gees?" I joked. "Better yet, how about 'You Be Illin' ' by Run—D.M.C?" We laughed hysterically.

"Better than 'Highway to Hell' by AC/DC," my sister added, which caused shrieks of laughter.

Eventually, after the playfulness was over, we hung up. As I closed the booklet and placed it back inside my backpack, I thought about how the most important question was missing. Whoever wrote the "Directive" hadn't been diagnosed with a life-threatening illness. If so, their perspective and questions would have included, "How would you like to be remembered?" There wasn't a single legacy-oriented question included. It was as if the "art of living" didn't exist. This booklet highlighted the "act of dying" instead.

I want to be remembered as a loving person. Someone who makes the world better by being in it. A person who can fill a room with laughter and positivity.

* * *

Coming up on my third chemotherapy appointment, my anxiety soared. When I went to the lab to get my blood tested 24 hours before treatment, I was down 12 pounds, bald, frail, and incredibly weak. I was in line at check-in, wearing my black ball cap, when I heard a woman complain behind me.

In a condescending and purposely loud voice, she asked, "Is there only one receptionist working this morning?" The answer was obvious, only one person was sitting behind the desk.

Complaining and openly expressing negativity tends to lead to a pack mentality. When one dog barks, other dogs chime in.

"It's ridiculous," the lady next to her griped. "It's like we don't have anything else to do today."

Oh, brother, I thought.

At the front of the line, the receptionist motioned me to come over. When I got there, although she had helped me twice before, this time, she acted differently. There wasn't a funny story about her granddaughter or what she did over the weekend. Maybe she was too busy to make small talk, but that didn't stop her the other two times.

She handed me a paper with a number on it, and as I turned to leave, I walked past the two lamenting women. Their eyes followed me, a mask of pity on their faces. As I pretended to browse through a magazine, waiting for my number to be called, I could still feel them staring.

And then it hit me: what I feared, had become a reality.

No longer was I the middle-aged woman with the cute Chuck Taylors, wearing funky jewelry or carrying a purse that people complimented. No, I was a full-blown cancer patient. *And that's why the receptionist didn't chat. She doesn't recognize me anymore. My appearance has drastically changed; she doesn't know who I am.*

With fixated stares, just when I thought I couldn't feel worse, one of the women leaned in and whispered something to the other. I knew it was about me by how their gazes flicked back in my direction. My already-shattered self-esteem splintered into what felt like irreparable slivers. There wasn't enough glue to reconstruct it.

What was worse than the staring, and the gossiping, was their scared expressions: contorted faces with furrowed brows, forehead wrinkles converging, and hopelessness in their eyes. They looked at me as if the cancer was winning.

What hypocrisy! Society pretends to offer support to cancer patients by labeling them with empowering words like strong, brave, and courageous, classifying us as fighters and warriors. But in reality, some people's actions prove otherwise. I didn't need strangers to treat me differently; I just needed them to show some respect and treat me like everyone else.

It was everything I could do to walk into the lab, get my blood drawn before my third chemo, and not break down. As soon as the phlebotomist placed a bandage on my arm, I grabbed my keys, dashed out of the medical building, and ran to my car. There was no end to this anytime soon. My appearance was only going to get worse, the pity looks would become more frequent, and I had to figure out a way to handle it.

How did Uncle Don handle the stares? Did he ever say anything to my aunt about it?

When I asked Aunt Marilyn over the car phone speaker, she paused for a full minute. I wasn't sure if she was trying to remember, find the right words, or didn't want to dredge up the painful memories.

"One day after his treatment," she told me, "I took him out to lunch at a restaurant. When we walked in the door, it was as if everyone stopped to stare."

"Did he notice?" I asked. *I noticed.*

"He never mentioned it, but he must have. He had limited strength and energy, so he probably didn't want to talk about it."

"What did you do?" *What should I do?*

"We ignored it. Time with him was too precious to ruin something special. But let me tell you, I realized something. The stares had nothing to do with Donald. The people stared because they were terrified. Terrified of getting cancer themselves. If Donald could get it, then they might."

Her profound words sank in, filling the gaping holes of my empty self-esteem. It was true. This wasn't about me but them. Under the look of pity was fear. Scared of their mortality, uncomfortable, entertaining the idea that someday they would die and cancer might be the cause.

"People need to be conscious as to how they react!" I vented.

"I agree," she said.

"They need to try to understand the situation and not feel sorry for us. Help support us. Believe that the outcome will be good. Millions of people have overcome cancer. Why do most people assume that death is the only way to the other side of it?" The more I talked about it, the more agitated I became.

"What can we do to change society?" My aunt's question wasn't an easy one to answer.

When we hung up, I had no idea how to fix it. It runs too deep. How can someone like me, sick with a weakened immune system, tired, and barely standing, alter the perception? Even if I came up with a brilliant idea, I didn't know if I'd have enough strength or energy to create real change.

The sun's heat penetrated my face through the windshield as I drove home. I basked in its radiance as if it might absorb my problems and carry them away. *The power of sunshine,* I thought, *fixes everything. As the closest single star at the heart of the solar system, it holds enough power to light up the entire world.*

I continued to focus on the freeway in front of me when suddenly: *That's it! The answer to changing the narrative around cancer is sunlight! Be the sunlight.*

From that point forward, whenever I received that look of pity, I'd respond with a genuine smile. A smile would prove I was okay, even in my worst physical condition. It would confirm that if life ever forced someone to walk three days in my shabby shoes, they could somehow be okay, too. It's not our physical appearance or ailments that define us; it's the energy we exert into the world.

And you might wonder, how do you have a genuine smile during such unfathomable times?

Focus on gratitude. I often choose five things (in that moment) that I am thankful for. And I guarantee ... those five things will ignite the internal spark of joy. They are five significant reasons to keep smiling.

TEN MONTHS

LET'S FACE IT; there's never a good time to get diagnosed with cancer. But an upcoming, monumental event makes it extra hard. Chris and David had hired a wedding photographer to capture every detail of their celebration. As the Matron of Honor, I knew there would be photos taken of me that might be housed in albums for years to come. I didn't want them to look at those photos and be reminded of my cancer diagnosis. If they did, my cancer diagnosis would live on forever.

I not only needed to look healthy but have hair on my head. *When will my hair start growing back?* It seemed like a silly question since I had just shaved it off, but the urgency was there since the countdown to her wedding was on.

There are several shampoos on the market that promote hair growth. I researched them online but given that Rhonda had told us during orientation to avoid herbal supplements or vitamins unless they were cleared by Dr. Santos, I was concerned that the products might affect the success of my chemotherapy. I read through the list of ingredients: minoxidil, polysorbate 60, and stearyl alcohol, trying to determine if they were harsh chemicals.

Unsure, I decided it was better to wait it out and grow my hair back the natural way, even though a part of me just wanted the peace of knowing for certain that in those photos, I'd have hair.

* * *

When I walked into the chemo room for my third treatment, I thought about my Uncle Gary, my mom's second oldest brother. This time, my treatment would be dedicated to him.

"Slay the dragon," he told me over the phone. He'd used this phrase to motivate himself to walk into the chemo room during his ongoing fight against bladder cancer.

Gary had the kindest soul I had ever met. There was a gentleness about him yet a dragon-slaying toughness at the same time. During his diagnosis, he took up woodworking, whittling small toy cars out of blocks of wood to hand out to children in the hospital's pediatric wing. Creating those toys became his life purpose.

As I settled into the recliner for my third round, I said in silence, *let's slay the dragon.*

The room that I once felt extremely uncomfortable in now became the one place in the outside world I felt normal. It brought comfort to be surrounded by my peers—other patients—who understood what it felt like to be diagnosed with cancer. Pity looks didn't exist within the walls. I was like everyone else, and the oncology nurses treated me kind with respect.

Thinking about my sister's upcoming wedding, I asked my nurse, "How long does it normally take for a person's hair to grow back after losing it?"

"Often, it starts growing back before the patient is finished with chemotherapy." Her answer gave me tremendous hope that my hair might come back sooner than later. Maybe *I'd* be one of those lucky patients.

After an hour had passed, an older woman with short curly brown hair entered the room and sat down next to me in the only open recliner. Nurses greeted her cheerfully, which suggested that even though she had a full head of hair, a healthy skin tone, and an abundance of energy, it wasn't her first time there.

"Evelyn," a nurse said, "it's so nice to see you!"

Evelyn's nurse started her IV and then walked away. Within seconds, Evelyn lifted herself out of her recliner and approached us, placing her hand on top of mine. My sister and I looked up at her, surprised.

"I was diagnosed with thyroid cancer for the second time," she offered. "During my first batch of chemo, I lost all of my hair." She then tilted her head down so I could get a view of the tight curls layered on top of each other. "But look at how much hair I have now."

"It looks great!" I told her.

She proudly stated, "All of this hair grew in only ten months." Then she patted my hand. "Don't worry, sweetheart, yours will grow back quickly, too," she said and smiled as she returned to her seat.

I appreciated her encouraging words but was also taken aback. She hadn't been there to hear my question to the nurse. And yet, hair growth was the only thing on my mind while sitting there.

"That's a lot of hair growth in ten months," my sister said quietly so only I could hear.

"How many months is it before your wedding?" I asked.

Chris counted each month out on a finger. "Ten months," she whispered. We held each others' gaze equally as astonished by the coincidence. "That's enough hair for a pixie cut," she added.

The Universe always provides when you need something. And that day, it sent me Evelyn.

INNER VOICE

"Bodies in motion, stay in motion," I said aloud to motivate myself to get out of bed.

If I didn't force myself to move the days following my third round of chemo, I was afraid I'd become too weak to walk. *Get up for a glass of water.* And so I would. *Take Stella outside.* I'd go down the street a block before the exhaustion got the best of me. But the point is, I did it. I listened to my body and yet, pushed forward just enough.

And then, a new feeling and side effect appeared: the urge to vomit. Hunched over the toilet, I waited. Nothing. I stared into the toilet bowl a little while longer. Nothing. I finally stood up, went to the sink, and splashed cold water on my face. When I looked in the mirror, I was stunned by my reflection.

Who is that? That can't be me, I thought, as some of the water droplets slid off my chin.

Yes, my hair was gone, and my face was a sallow, pale color. Looking like this, honestly, I could understand the pity stares that followed me everywhere I went. But when I saw my reflection that day, for the first time in my life, I was unrecognizable, even to myself.

Alone in the bathroom, I announced, "I am so ugly. Look at my bulbous forehead and bald head. I look more like an alien than a human being."

Woah.

And that act of self-cruelty stopped me. It was powerful to hear my own voice say those hurtful and mean words. *What if someone else said those exact things to me? Would I stand up for myself? Would I believe them?*

I tested the theory in the third person. "You are so ugly. Look at your bulbous forehead and bald head. You look more like an alien than a human being," I said, stepping away from my reflection in response.

Who talks to a cancer patient like that?

My inner voice had become my own worst enemy. Out of all the pitiful looks from strangers, none of them were as reprehensible as my own self-judgment. To fully embrace a new me, I had to silence the unkind inner voice and, instead, find an inner voice that was gentle with compassion.

Where do I start? An idea struck. I searched the house for Bruce and found him working in his office. As much as I knew his work was important, so was this brilliant idea.

"When I am feeling better before my next chemo, will you do me a favor?" I asked as he shifted his attention to me.

"Sure. What is it?"

"I'd like to document this moment of my life in pictures. Will you do a photo shoot of me?"

Surprised by my unusual request since I normally preferred to be behind the camera instead of in front of it, he replied, "Of course."

I need to feel comfortable with the way I look. Feel beautiful in my current physical state. A photo shoot seemed like the perfect way to not only build confidence but find a way to accept—*and embrace* — my new appearance.

* * *

Two weeks later, as the pattern on my side effects calendar predicted, I had enough energy for a photo shoot. Rummaging through my closet, I pulled out skirts, pants, shirts, and different outfit options, pairing them with accessories. Although I saved time by not having to style my hair, I took extra time applying makeup.

Bruce transformed the living room into a pop-up photo studio like he had the barbershop on our back patio. Reflectors were clipped to c-stands. A camera topped Bruce's tripod. He had opened the drapes to allow soft and flattering light in. I walked over and sat in one of our living room chairs, dressed in a white linen shirt, pants, and one of my favorite necklaces.

Bruce immediately kicked into career mode as if shooting a professional model instead of his wife. He directed me, composing each shot, telling me to move my body to the left or right, lean in, or turn my head a certain way. After 15 minutes and several poses later, he had taken over 200 photos.

"I think I got everything for this outfit. Want to see the shots?" He handed me the camera. "Make sure you like them before doing a clothing change."

Scrolling through the images, I was surprised by how many I liked. But beyond the flattering poses and angles, being the incredible photographer he is, he captured my essence. I could see it in the way my eyes lit up, in the softness of my smile, and in how I carried myself. Even feeling broken—and looking vastly different—I wasn't lost after all. It was the *me* that I recognized in photos of myself as a child, the *me* in the high school yearbook, and the *me* that graduated from college. What I thought was missing when I looked in the mirror had returned in every picture that he took.

That realization carried me through one clothing change after another.

On the last setup, I daringly told Bruce, "I'm going to take off my shirt and bra but keep shooting."

"You're going to what?" He backed away from his tripod, stunned. This was not the wife he knew. In the years we'd known each other, I'd never asked him to take a topless photo of me.

"Keep shooting," I told him.

But this would be the last chance to photograph my breasts before the lumpectomy. I wasn't sure how my right breast would look afterward and how my chest would look once the port was removed, but it needed to be documented. This was my transformation, and I wanted to capture it all.

REAL-LIFE SUPERHEROES

"You're always so positive," the receptionist told me with a smile as she typed my information into the computer at check-in before my fourth chemotherapy treatment.

"Really?" I said and smiled back.

"That's how I know you'll get through this," she said confidently as she wrapped a medical band around my wrist.

Hmm, I thought as I took a seat next to my sister in the oncology department's waiting room. *Am I positive?* Most of the time, I certainly didn't feel that way.

I had carefully constructed a determined and upbeat persona for THE SECRET SOCIETY when I shared the news about my diagnosis, so, maybe subconsciously, I had created a "positive" cancer-patient persona, too.

Why is there a perception that only positive people can overcome cancer? Is that a thing? Just because I am polite, act friendly, and appear to be emotionally and physically capable, does that somehow give me better odds?

"Jennifer, we are ready for you," a nurse said in the hallway, prompting my sister and me to grab our belongings and follow her back.

As I walked through the double doors on August 8, I thought of my friend, Krista. A talented photographer and artist, she passed away only months before I was diagnosed with the same disease. I made a silent dedication to her.

During Krista's journey to pay off some crippling medical debt, she sold a portion of her artwork. In support, I purchased a photo she had taken—a macro-shot of four pink flower petals with a water droplet on one of them. When I moved into our house in Palm Springs full-time, two months before I discovered the lump, I hung the framed photo on the wall of my office. Before my diagnosis, I thought of it as a beautiful picture, which it is. But post-diagnosis, I saw it differently. I recognized the water droplet as a symbol of her sadness. The choice of a pink flower was no longer a coincidence. Little did I know at the time that her art would, after my own diagnosis, inspire me to fight as hard as she did.

Throughout the day, as chemo—once again—ran through my veins, I glanced around the room, thinking about Krista and observing each of my peers.

I'm surrounded by superheroes, I thought. *Real-life superheroes.*

A superhero is someone with superhuman powers, and to me, a cancer patient is a real-life superhero with superhuman abilities. They bravely venture into the "known," sitting down in the recliner for another round of treatment, already understanding how severe the side effects will be. They listen and trust their gut. Some do treatment, some stop, and some choose a holistic route because that's what their instincts tell them. Not all fights with cancer are the same; neither are the superheroes who understand the ramifications of their decisions and yet, stay true to themselves and carry on.

Superheroes are of all ages, ethnic backgrounds, genders, and income levels. Some are social. Some are introverts. A few take naps while others are entertained by a morning talk show on their television screens. Some barely make it to the restroom in time. They tell jokes, strike up heartfelt conversations, share stories about their children, and know the value of a smile. Some hide their pain well, and some don't. Some are overly positive, and some can't say one positive thing. But regardless of their cancer-patient persona, this I know: they each appreciate life with a clear understanding of who and what they are fighting for, and they realize that life is too beautiful not to fight for another day of it. It doesn't matter if they cry, complain, spread joy, or remain silent; to sit among them is an honor.

SEEDLINGS

A HAWK LANDED in our backyard and wouldn't fly away.

When I came up for air 14 days after my fourth treatment, I felt as if my survival was a miracle. With the toughest side effects yet, God-willing, I made it through.

As I waited for the Nespresso to warm up for a cup of coffee, I glanced out the window and noticed the hawk perched on the block wall that separates our backyard from a sandy wash. It sat there without moving. Although it was nearly 30 feet away, I could see its black eyes staring right at me.

I tugged at Bruce's shirt when he entered the kitchen. "Look," I whispered as if the bird was a spy, listening.

"A hawk," he whispered back, as taken as I was. Hawks are common in the low desert, but in all the years we'd lived there, we'd never had one come so close.

We continued to gaze at the hawk as it studied us. It was like one of those staring matches where the first to blink, loses. It seemed the hawk was out for the win.

"What's it doing there?" Bruce murmured.

"I don't know," I said.

Sliding the patio door open, I stepped outside and clapped my hands loudly before quickly stepping back in and closing the door. The hawk, with its sleek body and striking plumage, didn't move.

"It's still there," I said, more to myself than Bruce.

Bruce finally grabbed his mug. "I'm going to paint some surfaces for the next shoot. Back to work," he said and headed into the garage.

"Me too," I said and left the hawk behind as I went into my office. But I couldn't push the hawk out of my thoughts even as I worked. A nagging feeling made me want to get up and see if it was still there. Each time I checked, it was.

Clearly, this isn't an ordinary hawk.

Hawks tend to stay up high, far away from people, swooping close only when they've spotted an ill-fated mouse or snake. I could feel that there was something important and special about this one. Its presence felt purposeful, even symbolic, and so I closed the contract I was working on and googled "hawk symbolism."

The first article I found said that hawks represent future planning, intuition, and protection. A hawk will show up to support a goal or mission, providing encouragement and strength to keep going. *Was it encouraging me to get through another two rounds of chemotherapy?* A different article described hawk symbolism as a messenger from the spiritual world. *Was it Krista, Grandma Wells, or Uncle Don? If so, what did they want to tell me?*

Back in the kitchen, I was peeking out the window for the seventh time when Bruce rushed in with wet paint on his hands. "I had a revelation. I know why it's here!"

"You do?!" I was excited to know.

"It's a sign. Our luck has officially changed. You're going to get well. Our lives will become normal again. I can feel it!" He spoke with such confidence and enthusiasm when he said, "This is the exact moment when everything starts to get better. A turning point. Trust me." I didn't know how to respond.

Before I could say anything, the hawk suddenly unfolded its majestic wings and took flight. It was as if Bruce's declaration gave it permission to leave; its mission to deliver the message was accomplished. We watched as it soared into the sky, circling once over the wash before disappearing in the distance.

* * *

The same day that the hawk was sent to deliver our perceived message of hope, Bruce's brother called with more discouraging news. I returned from my afternoon errands to find Bruce on the sofa, oddly quiet, with his chin dropped to his chest. I knew something was wrong, so I removed my ball cap and sat beside him.

Bruce muttered, "I spoke to Bob on the phone."

"What happened?"

"Cancer has spread to his lungs."

When Bob was younger, he was in a car fire. When the fire crew arrived on the scene, the smoke was so dense they couldn't even see Bob in the driver's seat. Luckily, they managed to extricate him from the car, but he suffered permanent injuries, including weakened lungs. Cancer has a habit of attacking vulnerable places, and this news was heartbreaking for Bob and the family.

I was silent. My words couldn't fix things or make Bob better. So, we just sat there. Without a sound happening around us, it was as if the world had become frozen in time.

Suddenly, Bruce's expression changed when he looked over at me. "Your hair is growing back!" My hand was immediately blocked by his when I reached up to feel it for myself.

"Are you sure?" I asked as Bruce rotated my chin with his fingers so he could examine the back of my head.

"And it's over here!"

"Are you serious?"

"It's so soft," he said as his fingers brushed over the curve of my skull, "like a newborn's hair."

"What color is it?"

"Black." I could feel his breath on my neck as he moved closer. "There are little seedlings and patches everywhere!"

I remembered my baby book. My mom had taped a lock of jet-black hair to a page inside. By the time I was a toddler, my hair had turned platinum blonde. But knowing that my hair was back, black again after 40 years, signified a rebirth.

I rushed into the bathroom to look in the mirror. I had to see it to believe it. Several tiny clusters of hair darkened part of my scalp. Patchy and uneven, they resembled circular shadows. I ran my palm over them in different directions, and no matter which way my hand moved, the strands felt soft, unlike the stubble I had expected. I couldn't stop smiling.

Suddenly happy and hungry, I went to the kitchen and pulled an applesauce cup from the fridge and a silver spoon from the drawer. I stood there, grinning, as I spooned golden applesauce into my mouth.

When Bruce walked into the room with a smirk on his face, I knew he had something witty to say.

"What is it?" I said, still beaming.

"You're my Gerber baby," he said, which caused me to laugh so hard I almost spit up.

THE HIDDEN GEM

THE CLOSER I got to my fifth treatment, the more I wanted to quit. I can count on one hand the few times I've called it quits in my lifetime. A bad job. A bad relationship. A friendship that went sour.

But I wasn't sure why I wanted to quit chemotherapy. Was it my instincts trying to protect me from a complete physical collapse, or was I scared to endure the debilitating side effects, which I knew would be worse from an accumulation of medicine? I needed a clear answer from my gut. One that I could rally behind with certainty and trust. But for some reason, my gut was asleep and no question or concern could wake it up.

And to top off the mental anguish, a new allergic reaction had surfaced. My eyes constantly watered, making both eyelids sore and puffy.

I. Was. Miserable.

Miserable from not knowing what to do or how to proceed. Miserable from more annoying side effects. Miserable from skyrocketing anxiety.

The night before my fifth treatment, I felt unhinged. By the time I woke up the following morning, my mind raced with reasons as to *why* I should not drive to L.A. and instead call it quits.

My tumor has shrunk. There's no need to terrorize my body and organs any longer. Cancer has been shut down already.

But when I told Bruce out loud, "I'm done with chemo; I've had enough," I didn't feel a sense of relief like I thought I would. In fact, I felt even more unsettled.

Bruce looked baffled. "At the beginning," he reminded me, "you told me you would trust your instincts. Your instincts told you to adhere to the advice of Dr. Hu and Dr. Santos. If what you're doing now is working, why change it?" He was right, and—*finally*—my gut confirmed it. I had to go.

My sister's car was parked in front of my mom's condo by the time I arrived. When I rushed over and opened the passenger door, Chris could tell something was off.

"What's wrong?" she asked as I threw my backpack on the seat and got in.

"I hate this so much. I don't want to do it again."

She looked over at me and said something so logical I had to accept it. "I know you hate it. But for the chemo to kill cancer, it has to be stronger than the cancer is. No wonder it's awful; it has to be."

To kill something as aggressive as cancer required numerous rounds of ammunition. The more ammunition I had, the better my chances of survival. I couldn't walk away; I had to stay and fight.

So when the time came to drum up enough courage to walk through the double doors for chemo number five, I dedicated the treatment to Bob. A wild-west kind of guy, I thought, *with guns blazing, let's fight like motherfuckers!*

* * *

At home that evening, I scrolled through several unread texts on my phone. At the end of the thread was one from my sister, which was strange since I was with her all day.

CHRIS: I KNOW IT'S WEIRD, BUT I WILL MISS GOING TO THE CHEMO ROOM WITH YOU, EVEN THOUGH I AM GLAD YOU'RE ALMOST DONE.

After my sixth and final chemotherapy, I no longer needed a sidekick to drive me to the facility for my monoclonal antibody therapy infusions. With only an hour-long infusion time and my appointment switching from the early morning to 1:30 p.m., it made sense that she focused on her work without interruptions. Coincidentally, the wedding planning was almost finished, too.

At the beginning of my journey, it was unfathomable to think that it would be possible to create special moments with my sister from inside the chemo room. But through the double doors was the rare opportunity to have the time and space we needed to plan her and David's wedding without any real distractions. What we shared there was special.

And although I once thought of the chemo room as a miserable place, my perception of it had changed. But that's the essence of the human spirit. We have the ability to adapt and create something positive and significant out of our hardships. We will dig through the piles of dirt and debris to find the hidden gem. That's who we are. That's what makes us human.

I replied to Chris:

ME: I KNOW EXACTLY WHAT YOU MEAN.

SURVIVOR'S GUILT

"I HAVE no idea how to survive this," I told my mom when she asked how I was feeling from the latest chemo side effects.

"Get through the day. Everyone can get through a single day," she replied. *Yes, treat each day as its own. It's the only way through,* I thought. "Break it down and make it small," she added, which was something she always said to give us the confidence to tackle something big.

During a follow-up with my surgeon, Dr. Hu was eager to check the size and density of *Feisty Righty* to see how well my treatment plan was working since Dr. Santos had told her there was a significant difference after only the first treatment. She pressed her fingers deep into my breast and moved her hand around as if searching for *something*, and that *something* she couldn't find.

Somewhat perplexed yet relieved, Dr. Hu stated, "I can no longer feel the tumor."

"Does that mean the cancer is gone?" I asked. *Please, God, let it be gone.*

"Well, we won't know if there's been a complete response,

meaning the tumor dissolved entirely until we remove the tissue during surgery. I'd like to schedule one more ultrasound once you're finished with chemotherapy. There's a window where the surgery should occur after your immune system has repaired itself and before the chemo is completely worn off, normally within three to four weeks."

"What about radiation?" I knew radiation was also a way to control cancer or a recurrence, and it was on the list of steps Dr. Santos had provided.

"You need to allow your body enough time to heal from the lumpectomy first, so usually it takes another three to four weeks to begin radiation after surgery. I'll set you up with a radiation oncologist to begin the process. Let's have you come back to see me after your sixth chemotherapy for a pre-op appointment." And before she left, she smiled and said, "The hardest part is almost behind you. Hang in there."

The glorious phrase, "You are cancer-free," was the only thing I wanted to hear since the day I was diagnosed. With Dr. Hu's comment, it felt as if one day soon, I'd hear those incredible words.

That night, I had a dream. I was walking through a dark tunnel toward a beam of golden light. Even though I could feel the cool earth beneath my bare feet, they were lost in the darkness. I kept walking closer to it. When I finally stepped into the bright light, as I felt its radiance on my skin, I realized I had made it to the other side of cancer.

I woke up feeling as if I had.

* * *

In September, Sunday afternoons are all about football. Bruce was raised in the Bay Area near San Francisco, so just like his father, he cheered for the 49ers. No matter where each family member was located geographically, it was guaranteed that the television would be on, the game would be playing, and everyone in the James family would be watching.

The phone rang at the start of the commercial break. Bruce muted the TV to hear his brother's voice. It was apparent Bob was also carrying on the family's tradition, so the break was an opportune time to make a quick call before the game resumed.

"Brute, how's Jennifer feeling?" Bob asked in his usual raspy voice.

"She's almost done with chemo. There's only one treatment left, and then she'll have surgery. Radiation will follow," Bruce said.

"Chemo is bad. That's why I refused it. But I've changed my mind and am left with no other choice. With chemo, my doctor says I have a year. Without chemo, only months. No one should ever have to hear the word *terminal*," Bob told us and immediately shifted the conversation to avoid further questions. "Can you believe the 49ers game today? And that bad call in the first quarter? Where'd they find these refs?"

Changing the subject couldn't lift the weight—*or impact*—of his devastating news.

* * *

Later that evening, I stepped outside. Optimistic about my own journey, it was disheartening to hear how Bob's road to recovery had veered off course. We shared the same goal, but that didn't mean the goal was obtainable.

I could feel the change in the air. The porch light flickered, and leaves fell from the trees. The smell of chimney smoke reminded me of Nebraska autumns. I zipped up my coat, but there wasn't just a chill from the falling temperatures. I had an internal chill that wouldn't go away.

And then ... came the guilt. So much guilt. I felt guilty for how well my journey was going compared to others. *Why me and not Bob? Why me and not Krista? Why me and not Uncle Don?* We all wanted to beat cancer, and yet, I was the lucky one.

It seemed ironic that I had survivor's guilt when I hadn't even been told I was cancer-free yet. Maybe it was Dr. Hu saying the worst was behind me. Perhaps it was the convincing "light at the end of the tunnel" dream. Maybe it was my instincts. But it felt as if my cancer diagnosis would one day be part of my past. And yet, Krista and Uncle Don were never blessed with the opportunity. And Bob's destiny was taking him further away from the place he wanted to be.

It struck me at that moment how easily the prosaic events in life continue with or without us witnessing them. Life keeps moving, regardless. Sunday afternoon football and lousy referee calls will outlive us all.

Bruce joined me on the patio. We watched the wind take whatever it wanted as it carried things away: a dried flower petal, a scrap of paper, and a blackbird's feather. It felt as if the wind's current represented the unpredictability of life.

"My brother is going to die," Bruce said, his voice soft with emotion. We sat for several more minutes as we listened to the wind bellow through the wash. And then, just like how his brother quickly changed the subject, he said, "I am so glad you're almost through this."

"Me too," I said, "but I will need time to heal."

"Physically?"

"Yes, but also mentally and emotionally. So much has happened in such a short amount of time. I've been caught up in the momentum of getting to appointments, and through treatments, there is no way to process what I went through until the physical part is behind me. I have so much more healing to do."

Bruce's phone rang; this time, it was his mom. "Did you hear the latest about your brother?" Panic filled her voice.

"Yes," Bruce said, "I spoke with him earlier."

"Call it mother's intuition," Betty stated, "but I knew at the start of the year it was going to be tough." And then she added, "We all have to make it through." When he didn't respond, she said, "Hear me? We all have to make it through."

If only it were that easy.

THE NEWCOMERS

THE CHEMO CHAIRS never sit unassigned for very long. As soon as one patient is finished with treatment, there's always someone newly diagnosed to fill the spot.

The last day of chemo felt like college graduation. Although there was no diploma, there was the same finality and sense that the future was wide open. A new chapter of my life was about to begin. Most oncology departments celebrate the momentous day with a bell to ring or gongs to whack with a rubber mallet. Patients sometimes order pizzas or bring in cupcakes to share with the group. September 19, represented the end of chemo for me, but there were 12 more non-chemotherapy infusions to go in the same place, so ordering pizzas would have to wait (which I'd prefer doing over ringing a bell or whacking a gong) until the very end.

To channel courage through the first five rounds of treatment, I made silent dedications to Uncle Don, Grandma Wells, Uncle Gary, Krista, and Brother Bob. The courage was already present on the sixth since it would be my last. I walked through the double doors with gratitude and confidence, motivated and ready.

I stood on the scale. My weight had dropped 21 pounds since the start of chemo, and I knew the last round of side effects would cause me to lose a few more, but I was relieved that my appetite would eventually return. Food would soon taste good again. I looked forward to dining out, gaining back a few healthy pounds, and being able to run errands without worrying about the sudden nausea that always came on at the most inconvenient times.

"How are you two going to celebrate?" the oncology nurse asked as she plugged a medicine bag into my port.

"I'm treating her to lunch," my sister said, as excited as I was. "Anywhere she wants to go."

"I think Italian sounds good." I knew a nice but not overpriced restaurant that made the perfect crescent-shaped, golden-brown calzones with just the right amount of cheese, sauce, and meat.

Our enthusiasm quickly dwindled when a young woman in her early twenties entered the room wearing cutoff shorts, a sweatshirt, and colorful knee-high socks. Two long brown ponytails swung from each side of her head. The nurse accessed her medical file on the computer while her boyfriend skirted around behind him, doing his best to look over the nurse's shoulder at the monitor.

"How does her bloodwork look?" the boyfriend asked, pivoting back and forth.

"Good. She's been cleared for her first treatment today," the nurse replied.

"How long do you think it'll take?"

"All day," the nurse confirmed, doing his best to focus on the young woman and the task of getting her ready for chemo. "You'll be more comfortable sitting in the visitor's chair next to her," he hinted.

"I'll sit down later."

My sister and I didn't talk or open a single bridal magazine. Instead, we sat there, observing as he hijacked her session, nervously shifting his weight and trying to take command of the situation he clearly knew nothing about. I couldn't help but wonder if the young woman regretted having him there. It was easy to see that the one visitor she could bring with her was causing her more stress and uneasiness than comfort. With only one spot to fill, choosing the right sidekick was critical.

After the young woman's blood pressure was taken, the boyfriend glanced at the reading and remarked, "That's pretty good." He looked over at her, "It's good, baby."

"Spray!" A different nurse yelled from across the room.

"I'll be right back," her oncology nurse stated as he rushed off with a metal can.

The boyfriend dropped to his knees. *Is he going to propose?* He removed each of her shoes and began to massage her socked feet. It was apparent her boyfriend was trying to help, but the young woman carried a fear that a foot massage couldn't fix.

Another couple entered the room minutes later. It was a husband and wife that looked equally as uncomfortable to be there. Unlike the pacing boyfriend, the middle-aged husband sat in the visitor's chair next to my sister as the woman took a seat in the recliner to my right.

More newcomers, I thought.

Being surrounded by two new patients reminded me of how frightened I was about my future on the first day of treatment. I was so scared to lose my hair, to experience the side effects (even though I wasn't sure which ones I'd have), and that my final days of life might be spent in that room.

"Amy," the husband urged, "we need to speak with the social worker. We must do it today."

Amy brought it up to the nurse. "Would it be possible to speak with the social worker? We have some work-related issues that need to be sorted out."

I glanced back at the twenty-something boyfriend, but

nothing had changed. He was still on his knees, massaging his girlfriend's feet, and by the sour look on her face, she wished he wouldn't.

"Sure," the oncology nurse told the middle-aged couple. "I'll call Debbie."

When Debbie arrived, the boyfriend finally relaxed enough to sit down, but Amy's husband now tapped his foot on the linoleum floor, unsettled.

The social worker asked Amy what she could help her with, but her husband jumped in before Amy's mouth could open. "We must pay our bills, which requires two incomes. With her job now being jeopardized, I need to keep working. She has treatments scheduled several times each week. There's no way I can take that much time off work. Tell us what to do." He was desperate.

"Who is your employer?" Debbie asked Amy. I remember my first meeting with her when she asked me the same question only minutes before handing me the "Advance Health Care Directive."

Amy broke into tears, dropping her head and covering her eyes with her hands. "Why me?" Those were the only two words she could get out, and she repeated them.

My thoughts spiraled back to May 1, the day I was diagnosed. I had silently asked the same question over and over again. *Why me?* It was all too familiar. And then I received the response ... *Why NOT you?*

I wanted to hug Amy. Tell her what I had learned during my journey. Let her know I understood what she was going through, and eventually, she'd finish chemo like I was. But making contact without emotionally breaking down myself would have been impossible. I still needed time to heal.

"It's nothing that you did," Debbie responded in a professional yet maternal voice. "We see so many new cases at younger ages. It's our environment."

It was the same bullshit answer the genetic counselor

provided when my tests proved that the cancer was not genetically linked. Was there some memo informing medical personnel what they *should* say when they didn't know *what* to say?

An overly bubbly friend of Amy's walked in through the large double doors with a plastic smile. I could tell it was put on as part of the "I'm here as support" show. As soon as Amy's husband saw her friend, he jumped out of his seat.

"I have to use the restroom," he told them. "I'll be right back." We could see tears in his eyes, but Amy and her friend couldn't.

"I'll let you both catch up," Debbie announced. "We'll finish our conversation later."

Amy's friend plopped down in the empty chair. "How are you doing?" she asked as the social worker walked away.

"Why me?" Amy sobbed. "Why me?" The "it's our environment" response wasn't cutting it for her either. Amy was trying to figure out more significant answers about karma, mortality, and the real cause of her misfortune.

I wanted to tell her that there would never be a solid answer as to why, that it's her destiny, as dreadful as it seemed. Fate had led her to the chemo room, as my fate led me to sit next to her on my sixth and final chemo. But somehow, she would find her way through. She was more powerful than cancer itself.

Her friend took a packet from her purse with two chocolate chip cookies. Tearing open the wrapper, she handed Amy one. Taking a bite of the other and with a full mouth of cookie bits, she said, "We're going to get through this together."

I smiled at my sister. "You said the same thing to me." She had raced up my mom's flight of stairs in hopes of rescuing me from a diagnosis. Her arms held me up when my legs buckled on May 1. When I had no clue how I'd get through it, she had an answer. Better yet, she meant it.

My sister smiled back. "And we did; we got through it together."

It now made sense why she volunteered to be my chemo side-kick. I understood why she was there to help me to the restroom when I was tethered to a bag of medicine or get my prescriptions and why she sat in the economy chair and waited with me. She intended to keep her promise. And she did.

That afternoon, I ate every bite of my celebratory calzone.

USE THE ANGER

I HAD NEVER CURSED out destiny before, but I hit a breaking point
when I woke up with my right eyelid glued shut from infection.
The gunk from the nonstop eye-watering made it impossible
to see.

Drenching a washcloth in warm water, I dabbed my infected
eye. When I looked down at the washcloth (with my one good
eye), a ball of yellow muck contained several of my lashes.

"No way! No way! This can't be happening!" I yelled,
completely panicked.

Up to that point, chemo hadn't robbed me of my eyelashes.
Since my hair had begun to grow again, I assumed my eyelashes
had somehow made it safely to the other side. It felt like the one
thing chemo hadn't touched. But I was wrong.

Still unable to see, I dabbed again. This time I barely touched
my eye, and when I removed the cloth, more lashes were stuck to
it. Only a few lashes jutted from my upper and lower lids with
noticeable pink gaps in between.

I turned on the faucet and watched my eyelashes swirl around in the sink basin before disappearing down the dark drain hole, in which I howled, "Fuck you!"

I was sick of being sick.

But as soon as the words escaped my lips, I felt the empathetic energy of my Uncle Don. He was watching, and his celestial presence made me feel embarrassed. The cancer had robbed him of his life, not his lashes.

I apologized to him.

But there wasn't any judgment toward me. All I could feel was his warm, unconditional love and a sense of tremendous peace and understanding.

He said in his voice, the one that still resided in my mind and heart, "Use the anger to keep fighting. Use it."

Just as quickly as I felt him there, he disappeared, leaving me speechless.

A NEW NORMAL

Uncle Don's advice worked. I leaned on his words—and his strength—to ease the suffering from the side effects brought on by my sixth and final chemotherapy treatment. Without another one to follow, my body would slowly begin to repair.

With the end of chemo, questions filtered in from THE SECRET SOCIETY:

"When do you think you'll attend photo shoots again?"

"Will it be weird to tell your clients about your diagnosis?"

"When can I see you now that the chemo is over?"

All great questions, but my physical, emotional, and mental states were in shambles. Initially, I, like my friends and family, believed that once chemo ends, the most challenging part of the cancer experience is over. But what I realized is that the challenges are still there but in a different way. Yes, it might be physically easier, but emotionally and mentally, things get more complex.

I felt lost and unsure about how to integrate back into my old life as the new me. *Where do I go now? What IS normal?*

"It'll take time," my mom told me over the phone, "but you'll figure it out. Don't go back to shoots until you're ready. You don't need to tell anyone about your cancer until you feel like you should. There's no pressure to do anything."

"*How* do I integrate back?" I asked her.

"My co-worker who survived cancer said she had to create a new normal. That's what you need to do. It'll be different than your old life, but that's okay. Create a new normal," she told me.

It sounded simple, but I didn't know where to begin. *Which things should I let go of from my past, and what should I hold onto? How do I keep the things that mattered most to me pre-cancer and move forward with a brand-new perspective on life?* It's as if someone instructed me to build a house, and yet, I didn't have a blueprint.

* * *

Over the next few days, while caught in a tornado of thoughts about my new normal, a brand new fear bore its way in. *What if my cancer is already growing back?* The more my side effects diminished, the more paranoid I became.

When scrambled eggs tasted good, I knew the chemo was vanishing from my system. When I was able to effortlessly gather my thoughts, I knew exactly what that meant. When I could wiggle my toes without numbness, I became extremely worried.

The chemo is almost gone. Now what?

Don't get me wrong, it was great that my body was repairing itself, but it scared me that chemo was no longer my protector. Vulnerable without it, it was the one weapon I knew that killed cancer.

Ironically, at the beginning of my journey, one of my biggest fears was having to do chemo. But now, the fear of not having to do chemo was just as terrifying. Unexpectedly, I had come full circle.

It left me even more confused about what my new normal

might look like. *Will fear always be a part of it? Will I constantly worry that cancer might return?* And if I had to become accustomed to living with this heightened level of anxiety, I didn't know how I'd become a better version of myself. *Will I spend the rest of my life being paranoid?* I didn't want fear, worry, and paranoia to follow me into my new normal, but I didn't know how to stop it.

"SIR, I CAN HELP YOU!"

WHILE I WAS TRYING to conceive of a 'new normal,' I continued to engage in the day-to-day activities that were getting easier to do now that the chemo side effects had diminished. So, without severe stomach issues, I went grocery shopping.

When we pulled into the parking lot, Bruce asked, "Do you want me to come with you?" He had to make a phone call, which I knew he could do from the truck.

"No. I'm feeling good." I told him. "Be right back."

The grocery store was busy with shoppers—and with my immune system on the mend but still not optimal—I hurried through the aisles and made my way to the check stand. Only three lanes were open, and with the older man in front of me slowly taking quarts of ice cream from his cart and placing them on the conveyor belt, the line behind me began to grow. Eventually, another checker arrived to open a fourth stand.

I heard a man's voice say, "Sir, I can help you over here!"

I didn't think anything of it. Technically, I was next, but the gentleman in front of me was about to swipe his credit card, and if they offered the newly opened line to someone else, so be it.

I heard the same voice again, "Sir, I can help you!" But this time, a tap on my shoulder followed. I turned around to find the employee standing behind me, a look of shock on his face.

"I am so sorry," he stammered, unsure what to do next.

I registered his reaction and only then realized that with my ball cap and limited hair beneath it, he had thought I was a man, only to discover that I was a pale, gaunt-looking, cancer-stricken woman with thin eyebrows and a few sparse eyelashes, once I turned around.

I saw the faces of the customers standing in the long line behind me, watching the situation. As soon as I made eye contact, they pretended to be busy. A woman fiddled with something in her purse. Another lady stared down at her grocery list. A man ran away to grab something he had forgotten.

A wave of humiliation washed over me. Even though I knew it was an innocent mistake, with my self-esteem barely hanging on, it was a massive blow that no apology could fix. Despite my vow to smile in response to the looks of pity, I couldn't muster anything more than holding back the tears that threatened to burst free and cascade down my face.

Stay calm. Breathe, I told myself.

He motioned for me to go with him over to the next check stand. I could feel the gazes follow me as I followed him. I didn't want to, but I needed to get out of there quickly. It took everything I had to hold it together, and I knew I couldn't keep it up for very long. The young employee repeatedly apologized, which only extended the length of the transaction and made me feel more desperate.

As soon as my credit card was approved, I grabbed the bags of groceries off the stand and headed to the exit without taking my receipt. I heard the cashier yell, "Have a great day!" *The day was great before you ruined it.* Despite knowing it was an honest mistake and watching him apologize profusely, I felt angry toward him for embarrassing me.

After bolting across the asphalt to the truck, I threw the bags into the back and climbed into the passenger seat. Bruce was finishing his call, so I sat quietly, replaying what had just happened in my mind.

"All good?" Bruce asked when he hung up.

"Fine." I kept it short and didn't tell him about the incident. It was my way of trying to let it go. The more I talked about it, the more I thought about it. I had already accepted that cancer had taken my hair, my health, my time, and all sense of confidence in what I believed was a reliable future, but I hadn't considered it might make people question my gender.

But even doing my best to forget the "sir" comment, I felt disappointed in society. I was disappointed in stereotypes and that women are expected to have pretty hair and long eyelashes. Without them, you're often viewed as less of a woman.

Late that night, I was still thinking about the horrible mishap when Bruce pulled back the sheets and settled into bed next to me. "You know," he told me, "I don't care how your hair looks when it fully grows back. I don't care if you ever have hair again." It was oddly out of the blue, as he had no idea what had happened at the grocery store earlier. "As long as I have you in my life, that's all that matters."

His comment couldn't have come at a better time. I closed my eyes and finally let the employee's mistake go. That man didn't matter. The man who mattered was the one that fell asleep next to me each night and loved me, for me. And isn't that what we all want in life, to be loved for not what we look like but who we truly are?

POETIC HAPPINESS

"IT'S STILL THERE," the radiologist said after finishing my ultrasound.

"What is?" I asked, completely confused.

"The tumor," she stated, turning from the monitor to look at me.

My heart dropped. "How can that be?" I'd felt so confident that things were moving in a positive direction.

With her ink pen, she pointed at a speck on the screen. "Right here. It's teeny. About the size of a pea." Then she stepped back so I could get a better glimpse.

Sure enough, there it was. *Feisty Righty* was much darker than the other tissue surrounding it. I wanted it to be a mistake. Maybe the radiologist was incorrect about what she was seeing, or the pea-sized dark speck was some fluky thing caused by a faulty ultrasound wand.

"But Dr. Hu told me seventeen days ago that she could no longer feel it," I said, trying to persuade her to change her prognosis.

"That's because it's deep inside the tissue near your lung. It would be difficult to feel at this point."

"Does that mean I still have cancer?" I asked. Understandably, I hadn't been told I was cancer-free, but in my mind, I'd chosen to believe the cancer was pretty much gone, if not already.

"Not necessarily," she said, toggling back and forth between two black-and-white captures. "Pathology will need to confirm whether cancer cells are present when they test the tumor after surgery."

Feisty Righty was turning into one of those monsters in a horror movie that keeps getting shot, stabbed, and run over and can still drag itself to its feet to wreak havoc on its victims. After everything I did to kill it, the tumor wouldn't disappear.

As I left the facility, my mind drifted back to my tumor's documented location and how it still existed. I'd become too confident. I even felt guilty for being lucky when I wasn't really lucky at all. I'd skipped ahead to a place I wanted to be rather than acknowledging the place where I really was. As much as I had convinced myself that the cancer journey was coming to a close, there was a chance I was nowhere close.

When I got home, I felt as if I had fallen deeper into the tunnel's darkness, away from the glorious light of the other side. And, of course, the "what if's" reappeared. *What if I have to do more chemo? What if I can't attend my sister's wedding now? What if all the progress wasn't good enough?*

Bruce found me at my desk. He walked into the office to ask, "Any birthday suggestions for the big forty-two?" not knowing that my mind was spinning with fear. With all that I had put him through, I didn't want to tell him about what had transpired in case I was overreacting. *Please let me be overreacting.*

"Thanks, honey, but I'm good. You don't have to get me anything this year," I finally told him.

What I wanted, money couldn't buy. I desperately needed a

surgery date determined by Dr. Hu to remove the tumor. A bottle of champagne or a new pair of leather boots wasn't going to cut it. I wanted *Feisty Righty* gone.

"I have to give you *something*," he said.

"That's sweet, but I really don't need anything."

He didn't look convinced.

* * *

I was still feeling uncertain about my future when I was back in the chemo room five days later for my first monoclonal antibody therapy infusion without chemotherapy. The cancer journey is unpredictable. One day, I was elated, high on a cancer-free future. The next day, stuck, drowning in a sea of it.

"No sister today?" the oncology nurse asked. I didn't have the energy to make small talk, so I shook my head. "What's next for the wedding?" I could tell she was trying to find a subject that excited me, and my sister's wedding always worked.

"Bridal dress shopping," I said, but it was evident that I was still under a cloud of despair and unwilling to crawl out.

She smiled as she examined each side of my head. "What's that I see? Is that hair?!"

And without realizing it, I said loudly with untamed enthusiasm, "Yes, my hair is growing back!"

I was loud. Too loud. Embarrassed, I hunkered down in the recliner as everyone in the room glanced over simultaneously. As I looked around, one superhero wearing a cap with an embroidered palm tree on the front, smiled. I smiled back. Another lovely woman wearing a Gucci headscarf smiled. I smiled again. And then a man wearing a sporty ball cap flashed a grin in my direction. They just kept smiling and smiling.

Was my abrupt response THAT funny?

And then it hit me. They weren't responding to my boisterous voice or unexpected outburst but to what I had said. If my hair was growing back, it was a reminder that theirs would, too. The simple phrase, "My hair is growing back," in the chemo room, is as powerful as an eloquent verse of poetry.

Move over, Robert Frost; we have hair.

"THAT" WOMAN

I walked into the dining room after my pre-op appointment with Dr. Hu to find a small cake and a bouquet of wildflowers on the table. A *Happy Birthday* banner draped from wall to wall.

"Well," Bruce asked, "did you get a surgery date?"

"I did!" He gave me a high five and knew that my birthday wish had come true. "October twenty-fifth!"

"That's wonderful!" he replied, pulling out a knife, a couple of forks, and plates. "What did the surgeon tell you?" As I sat down at the table, he grabbed a pint of vanilla ice cream from the freezer and brought it over.

"There's a chance they might not get it all, and I may need a second surgery, depending on the margins. She said that my armpit area, where the lymph nodes will be removed, can sometimes take longer to heal than the breast, and I may experience numbness in the armpit area, which can be permanent if there's nerve damage." I sliced into the thick white frosting with the knife. "But I know Dr. Hu will do her best, so I am confident."

Moments after my little celebration, the phone rang. It was my aunt belting out the birthday song.

"Guess what?" she asked after the last note.

"What?"

"Since October is *Breast Cancer Awareness* month, I have a friend who would like to sponsor you through her company."

"Sponsor me? For having breast cancer?"

"Yes! Each employee selects one person diagnosed with breast cancer, and the company sends them a care package filled with free stuff. She picked you!" I didn't know what to say or which was worse—the fact that she leaked my coveted secret or that I felt completely embarrassed by the gesture.

"But they don't know me," I said, offended.

"I know. But you'll receive some new and free stuff. That can't be bad, right?" The joy in her voice waned as she realized I wasn't as excited as she was.

"But I don't need new stuff," I huffed. "Have your friend send the care package to someone who needs it." For whatever reason, this gesture triggered a brash reaction, which stemmed from something much deeper, far beyond a leaked secret or feeling embarrassed.

We both sat in silence on opposite ends of the line. She was shocked by my lack of gratitude, while I was surprised by my unleashed hostility. The only noise between us was the buzzing of bad reception.

Why did I react like that? I thought.

"I can tell her not to send you anything. It was never meant to upset you. We just thought you deserved something special."

Her golden retriever barked in the background. It filled another round of awkward silence, which gave me time to calm down. I had allowed my rocky emotions—and ego—to get in the way of a kind and thoughtful gesture.

"Have her send it," I finally announced calmly. "It really is okay."

"Are you sure?"

"Yes. Thank you for thinking of me."

Over more barking, she yelled, "I'll give her your mailing address," and abruptly ended the call.

With the phone still in hand, I felt awful. *Why am I so upset over a care package?* The notion had somehow added salt to a wound I didn't even know existed. It's okay to feel and show emotions, but I knew they stemmed from something deep down inside that needed to be heard, recognized, and accepted.

THE SECRET SOCIETY had sent numerous gifts throughout my treatment. Not once did I feel upset. If anything, I was incredibly grateful. *What makes this gift different?*

Under my breath, the words, "I hate being 'that' woman," escaped.

There it was. That was why. I felt like 'that' woman. A woman defined by nothing more than her diagnosis. My aunt's friend didn't know anything about me. She didn't know my favorite color or my middle name. To her, I was just a woman with cancer she could sponsor.

When cancer takes over your life, you lose so much—your identity, your confidence, your belief that there's some permanence in the world. Cancer becomes everything. Even after you psychologically separate yourself from the tumor invading your body, it dictates so much of your life. Tired of being 'someone with cancer,' I just wanted to be Jennifer again.

Three days later, a cardboard box appeared on my doorstep. When I opened it, it contained a small basket, a throw blanket, a bathrobe, and a bottle of bubble bath inside. A note was attached to the neck of the bottle.

It read:

WISHING YOU THE OPPORTUNITY TO RELAX DURING SUCH A DIFFICULT TIME. THINKING ABOUT YOU AND SENDING WELL WISHES.

WITH LOVE — DEBRA

This gift was absolutely wonderful. There was nothing pitiful about the basket of goodies. It was as thoughtful of a gift as I'd given Bruce on our anniversary—an opportunity to get away from the stress for a little while. I felt even more embarrassed for reacting the way I did and realized difficult times are easier when a fellow human reaches out to do something kind, whether you know that person or not. And as much as our egos may become wounded, a simple "thank you" is often the best response.

I put on the robe, curled up in the blanket, and immediately felt better.

ADIOS, FEISTY RIGHTY!

"*Na na na na, na na na na, hey hey hey, goodbye!*" I sang the lyrics to the 1969 Steam song as my mom and I cruised north along the 405 Freeway to the hospital for my outpatient surgery. A breakup song seemed appropriate. Instead of kicking a man out of my life, I was ready to kick *Feisty Righty* out of my breast for good. I had been its host for five months and 25 days, and even though I had no clue what its lifespan was before that, I was tired of toting it around.

The first pre-surgery step was a scheduled wire localization with the tallest doctor I had ever seen. Dr. Char could have easily spent his days dribbling a basketball up and down the court, but on this particular day, he was preparing to insert a wire into my breast to pinpoint the tumor's exact location for Dr. Hu.

"I'll use local anesthesia and numb the area first," he informed me, crouching to look me in the eye. "Instead of lying down, you'll sit up with your breast compressed between the plates of the mammogram machine. Dr. Hu will remove the wire after surgery. If you feel like you're going to pass out at any point, please let me know."

Why would I pass out?

Once a nurse had positioned my breast between the two plates, Dr. Char threaded a thin, flexible wire through a needle and then pierced the needle into my breast. A flood of wooziness made my skin clammy. *Mind over matter,* I told myself. But even as I tried to focus my attention on the heavy arm of the mammogram machine, the ceiling lights morphed into octagons, and the room spun. *Mind over matter. Don't pass out. Mind over matter,* I repeated silently to myself.

Suddenly, it was as if I couldn't swallow my spit fast enough, and I heard my voice say, "I feel dizzy," which was an extreme understatement.

One of the nurses rushed over and pressed a button to lower the back of the bed so I could lie down. Even in a supine position, my vision stayed fuzzy, and nausea made my stomach rumble.

"Her lips are turning blue!" the nurse yelled to the group. I had no idea what it meant, but it sounded terrible.

An icepack was pressed onto my forehead. The rush of cold steadied the spinning, but saliva kept filling my mouth. I tried to swallow faster, but I couldn't keep up. I closed my lips to keep the spit from dribbling.

"Do you have cottonmouth?" Dr. Char asked, wondering why my mouth looked oddly clenched.

"There's too much saliva," I gurgled and then quickly announced, "I think I am going to throw up!"

Like a linebacker, a different nurse pushed the others aside, scooping up a wastebasket and leaping toward me. Feeling the edge of the trash can against my chin was the permission I needed to heave. I gagged, but nothing came up. I gagged again, but still nothing.

"We've seen this before," Dr. Char said, and I felt his giant hand on my back. After several more gags, my vision became clear, and I sensed my body temperature drop. "Maybe I shouldn't warn patients that they might pass out. It's like I give them the idea to do it," he said, smiling.

I looked over at the linebacker, who still held the empty wastebasket. "And you," I said, "you shot over here at a record speed with that thing," which made her and everyone else laugh.

Slowly, I began to feel better, so Dr. Char said, "Let's continue."After several minutes of inspecting his work, he seemed pleased. "It's perfectly placed. Let me tape the wire down and finish up."

One of the nurses guided me down a short hallway to a different room, where another doctor went about injecting a blue-colored contrast dye into my areola in preparation for the sentinel node biopsy.

"Dr. Hu will use a gamma detector to identify the lymph nodes in which the dye has accumulated," he said. "She'll only remove the nodes where the tumor has drained."

"How many nodes are normally removed?" I asked, unable to feel anything due to Dr. Char's anesthesia.

"Usually, they remove one at the minimum, five max. The fewer nodes removed, the less likely you'll experience lymphedema, which is when too much fluid collects in the tissue."

As soon as he was finished, an orderly entered with a wheelchair. He pushed me up to the surgery area and dropped me off in the pre-op room at bed #14. In numerology, 14 is often associated with personal freedom. It seemed appropriate since I'd soon be free of *Feisty Righty* forever.

When my mom walked in to visit, I was so full of anti-inflammatory and pain meds I swore her blonde hair glowed like an angelic halo. I saw her smile before everything went black.

* * *

"Jennifer?" I heard a voice say. "Are you able to wake up? The surgery is over."

My eyes didn't want to open, but when they finally did, I was blinded by bright fluorescent lighting. The nurse handed me a couple of crackers and a glass of water. Oddly, since I hadn't eaten before surgery, I felt as if I could consume an entire box of them.

Over the phone, the nurse called my mom. "You may come to see Jennifer now."

When she walked in, her hair no longer glowed.

"Dr. Hu said it went well," my mom told me as she kissed my forehead. "She'll have the results back within the week."

As I dressed to go home, I was tempted to peel off the square bandage that covered my right breast. As much as I didn't want to look, I was curious whether there was a scar or even a deformity behind it.

But not today. Today, I need to bask in the relief that Feisty Righty is no longer inside of me. Smeared on a glass slide in a pathology lab, lost and dead without its host, it could no longer dictate my life. And in the long-drawn-out battle between us, I felt like *I* had finally won.

NOVEMBER 2

NATURE IS AN OUTSTANDING TEACHER.

As I sat on a rock in Joshua Tree National Park, watching Bruce take snapshots of possible locations for an upcoming photo shoot, the sun's heat felt therapeutic on my skin. Only three days after surgery, my right breast and armpit were sore, but the pain was tolerable.

Brush and craggy Joshua trees sprawled in every direction, and an outcrop of boulders towered beside me, jutting into the cyan sky. The afternoon sun bore down on the dimpled faces of the rocks, creating a shape like some see in the clouds: a bird in flight, a man wearing a tall hat, and a woman's body.

The park becomes even more populated in November when the days shorten and nights cool the desert sand. VW buses, cars, and jeeps rolled in. Hikers with walking sticks and rock climbers plotted routes. Even with all the activity, like a magnet, my eyes were constantly drawn back to the rock formation.

It amazed me that it had survived over four billion years, and I was only 42. It withstood torrential rains, unrelenting heat, and frigid nights. Each year, its appearance changed slowly and

237

imperceptibly, carved by the swirling wind and sand. And yet, it was uniquely beautiful. So beautiful that millions of visitors arrived each year to see it.

This boulder holds truth, I thought. *It has survived. Through each storm, it has become more unique and more beautiful in the process.*

A sharp ache pinched my right breast. I placed my hand on it and could feel the thick gauze they'd put on during surgery. I still couldn't help but wonder what was left behind. What would be revealed?

I thought about the similarities between me and the boulder. Millenniums of harsh storms had altered its surface, and a severe illness had altered mine. The boulder stood to face the challenges, and so had I. It could not hide from the sharp, whipping sand; I couldn't hide from the malignant cells that chose to attack me. Its distinctiveness comes from its ability to adapt, as does mine and yours.

"Are you ready to go?" I looked up to see Bruce standing in front of me.

As we drove down the 10 freeway on our way back to Palm Springs amid the fields of gigantic wind turbines, I began to feel more confident. Confident in my new appearance, regardless of any breast deformities. Confident in building a new normal. I felt confident that I could overcome any obstacle I might face in the future. Inspired by the boulder, I'd somehow withstand the storm, too.

With the same steadfast resolve I shared with the boulder, I walked into Dr. Hu's office eight days after surgery to get the pathology results.

Embrace the journey, I reminded myself.

When Dr. Hu entered the exam room, for the first time ever, I didn't feel anxious or nervous. In fact, my blood pressure was normal and didn't skyrocket. I had confidence about my well-being that I had never felt before.

So when she announced, "We received the results for both the tumor and tissue, along with the extracted lymph nodes," I took a deep breath and listened. *Whatever is supposed to be will be. And no matter what, I'll make it through.* "There are no cancer cells present," she said.

Tears rolled down my cheeks. It was as if my body understood the impact of her words before my brain could comprehend them. Every healthy cell inside me rejoiced. A battle was won as I finally stepped into the warm and embracing light of the other side.

I made it. We did it. The dragon was slain.

Dr. Hu handed me a tissue. "I know it's been a tough road for you," she said as she wrapped her arms around me in a hug. "Congratulations!"

On my way out of the office, Katja hugged me too, and I thanked her for connecting me with Dr. Santos. Without her, the outcome might have been different. Chris was in the waiting room, and I motioned for her to follow me out into the hall. There for emotional support; when she saw the glaze in my eyes, I could tell she was worried.

"What happened?" my sister asked.

I muttered, "It's over," still in disbelief. "It's over," I repeated as more tears streamed down my cheeks. "I can't believe I'm cancer-free." We then shared a "movie" moment where every-thing and everyone continued to move around us as we embraced one another in stillness.

Several dates have impacted my life, but two will always stand out: the day I was diagnosed with Invasive Ductal Carcinoma on May 1 and November 2, when I became cancer-free. One of the worst days of my life brought one of the best, with a battle to survive in between. My role had shifted from fighting cancer to preventing it from coming back.

I still wonder about the day that my cells went haywire and cancer started growing. I also wish I could pinpoint the exact moment when the cancer cells were no longer inside the tumor. Was it the day Bruce and I saw the hawk? Was he correct when he said, "It's a sign. This is the exact moment when everything starts to get better. A turning point," or was it the night I dreamt about walking through the tunnel to reach the other side of the disease? When did the last cancer cell shrivel up and die? Unfortunately, I'll never know.

If I'd had a megaphone, I would have blasted the news from a mountaintop in every direction, "I am cancer-free!" But without a mountaintop or megaphone, I reached out to THE SECRET SOCIETY to tell them, one by one. They congratulated me on the phone and through numerous messages.

That evening, before bed, I received a text from Lily that read:

LILY: It feels like the weight of the world has been lifted when I heard the news.

She was right. I could feel the difference in my body, too. For the first time in six long months, I could take in a full breath of air. Every muscle was relaxed. My shoulders dropped into their normal position. The pre-cancer lightness in my body had returned.

Technically, a cancer patient becomes a cancer survivor from the minute they are diagnosed until the end of their life. But on May 1, when Dr. Fez informed me of my diagnosis, I didn't feel like one. I didn't feel like a survivor through the numerous biopsies, mammograms, scans, and chemo treatments. But finally, with Dr. Hu's news, I not only accepted but embraced the title.

Today, I am a survivor, just like the rescued kitten.

PART THREE
BEYOND

GLOWING HUMOR

IT WAS time to remove the bandage covering my right breast. *Remember the boulder's beauty in Joshua Tree National Park,* I reminded myself as a way to mentally prepare.

As I carefully peeled away the adhesive tape and layers of gauze and padding until I reached the final layer, I was grateful for what I saw. My breast was still round and plump, even though tissue had been removed. Dr. Hu's incision was strategically placed around the outer edge of my areola—where there were tiny bumps to disguise the stitches. There were no scars jutting across the bottom, top, or side of my breast. Although it didn't appear quite the same as it had pre-surgery, Dr. Hu's precise work was masterful.

* * *

Almost two weeks later, waiting in the exam room at the radiation facility, I could see out the window the famous white letters of the HOLLYWOOD sign. And when Dr. Tanaka, my radiation oncologist, walked in for our meet and greet, her trendy appearance confirmed that I was, in fact, in Hollywood. What fascinated me the most, beyond her choppy black hair, ankle boots, and funky glasses, was the lightning bolt pin attached to her white coat, which seemed lightheartedly apropos.

She had me lift my right arm to confirm my range of motion. Thirteen days after my lumpectomy, my armpit region hadn't completely healed, although my breast felt back to normal. As I lifted my arm, it felt like it was attached to a thick rubber band.

"Can you extend it higher? Try placing it closer to your right ear," she told me. I dropped my right ear toward my bicep without thinking. "That's cheating," she said with a laugh. "Try again. Keep your head straight and only move your arm." I tried, but nothing happened. "You can relax now," she told me as she sat down in her chair. "Your range looks pretty good. To begin radiation, you must be able to place your arm back beside your ear and hold it there. With a little more time to heal, you should be able to do that without physical therapy."

Radiation was now the last unknown. I wondered if it would hurt being radiated and how severe the side effects might be. Anxious for her to explain the details, I listened carefully as she handed me a sheet of paper with, I assumed, the information she was about to explain.

"Radiation is a local therapy that uses high-energy waves to break the DNA inside the cells, forcing cancer to stop growing or coming back," she stated.

My new protector! A sense of relief washed over me. Some patients only use radiation after breast surgery to beat cancer, so if it can protect them, then it should prevent a recurrence for me.

She continued, "Your personalized plan includes twenty therapies over four weeks, Monday through Friday. For fifteen of the therapies, we will focus on the entire breast, part of the lung, and the armpit section where the lymph nodes were removed. After that, we will do five targeted boosts focusing on the area where the tumor was. Plan on being at the facility for thirty minutes each day. The radiation portion is short, less than two minutes, but you'll need time to get checked in, change, and then have the therapist position you properly."

"When do you think I'll start?"

"Before we do anything, we must define the area in which the radiation beams should effectively reach. Two different high-energy sweeps will cover your entire breast. This requires in-depth documentation so the machine's mapping can be customized to your chest and breast size. After that, we must do a trial run to check for accuracy."

Motioning to the paper in my hand, I asked, "Are there any bad side effects?" I figured that even though they were all listed, Dr. Tanaka would be able to explain them in more detail.

"Depends. Short-term side effects include pigmentation issues, similar to a suntan. Your skin may feel tight, like a sunburn. But if your skin blisters, please call my office. I can prescribe a cream to help. Fatigue is quite common, too. As for long-term side effects, a type of skin cancer may develop five to ten years down the road." *Great,* I thought, *prevent cancer by possibly causing a different type of cancer.* "Your ribs will be extremely brittle. One fall might break them, so be careful not to trip. And you may have trouble breathing since the radiation covers part of your lung. If you experience breathing issues, call me. That's pretty much it. Any other questions or concerns?"

"No," I said, relieved that the listed side effects could fit on a single sheet of paper instead of being housed in a blue binder.

And before she left, she said one last thing, "In case you were wondering, you can still be around pets, babies, kids, and even your husband without radiating them. It's not that type of therapy."

"Good to know," I said as her tiny ankle boots marched her out of the room.

Once she was gone, I laughed. Thinking about being radioactive was hilarious. Of course, it was a serious concern for a lot of patients that undergo various radiation therapies, but I couldn't help but picture myself as a green-glowing bug zapper that people could see coming from miles away in the dark. I'd pet Stella with an accidental zap. Give Bruce an electrifying kiss. Like how the mythical King Midas touched objects to turn them to gold, I'd have the power to make things glow.

As I changed out of my medical gown, I thought about how humor plays an important role in any *how-in-the-hell-will-I-survive-this* obstacle. And laughter, well, it's essential, like drinking water or exercising or getting enough sleep. Whether it was the idea of replacing my hair with a Marie-Antoinette wig, assigning my tumor an ineffectual name, or joking about which songs I wanted played at my funeral, there is no doubt that laughter was there to pull me through.

And then I realized something: humor needs to take center stage more often in my new normal. Life doesn't have to be as serious as we think it should be. It can be a comedy. After all, life is *supposed* to be fun. That's why we signed up to live it.

A BREAKTHROUGH

AFTER MONTHS of collecting ideas from magazines, it was time to take the bride-to-be out to try on gowns. In less than six months, Chris and David would marry, which required the perfect dress, alterations, matching shoes, a veil, and jewelry. As the Matron of Honor, I sent out handmade invitations to a select few: her future mother-in-law who lives in Arizona, our mom, and both brides-maids, Utaiwan and Daya (my sister's best friend from high school who lives in Denver).

Appointments were staggered at three different bridal boutiques, so if Chris couldn't find "the perfect dress" at the first, we were prepared to continue the search after lunch.

At the first shop, the manager buzzed us in as we stepped into a utopia of elegant gowns, each meticulously adorned with hand-sewn embellishments, beading, delicate lace, and some with flowing tulle. As we browsed the racks, a bridal specialist ushered my sister around the store, exploring options. She gathered three gowns and whisked Chris away into a dressing room. The rest of us wandered over to a cluster of chairs to sit and wait.

The first dress my sister walked out in was a simple yet elegant, stark white A-line with spaghetti straps. It was flattering, but it wasn't *the one*. We nodded in approval, and she disappeared into the dressing room.

The second time she came out, she wore a gorgeous backless ball gown and a stunning smile to match. She stepped onto a riser so we could see how the beading on the bodice glittered in the floor-to-ceiling mirrors as she twisted back and forth.

"Oh honey," my mom gushed, "you look beautiful!"

David's mother added, "It's incredible. You look amazing."

"Damn, girl, you look hot!" Daya shouted, which made us all laugh.

Utaiwan hopped out of her seat and walked around the dress, checking to see if the craftsmanship met the highest standards. "I think it's perfect, too," she finally said with a smile.

I had never seen my sister spin before, not even as a child. Spinning wasn't her thing, so when she twirled around in that beautiful 'Casablanca' at the bridal boutique, I knew how the dress made her feel.

Admiring her reflection, she turned to me to ask, "Sis, does it look as good as the dress in the August issue?" She was referring to a picture in one of her magazines that we both fell in love with during those many hours we spent in the chemo room.

"Even better," I remarked. "It's incredible."

The bridal specialist asked my sister, "What do you think?"

"I don't think I need to try on anything else," Chris said, still beaming.

Inspired by our mutual binge-watching of *Say Yes to The Dress*, I asked her the show's famous final question, "Are you saying yes to the dress?"

"Yes!" she announced, prompting us to clap and take turns giving her hugs.

After my mom surprised her by purchasing the gown as a present, we drove in high spirits over to a Tuscany-inspired restaurant in Westlake Village for lunch. On the covered patio surrounded by fragrant and colorful flowers, we sipped white wine and listened to Christine divulge the activities planned during the week-long trip to Jamaica. I couldn't help but feel her dream was close to becoming a reality.

After the waiter had taken our orders, Daya looked at me from across the table and asked, "So what is the biggest thing you have learned from having cancer?"

To her, my diagnosis was new. Hours before she boarded the plane to Los Angeles, we told her, hoping to minimize the shock from how much weight I had lost and how I no longer wore a ponytail but a ball cap instead.

The table grew silent as everyone waited with anticipation for some profound takeaway, but it was impossible to summarize everything I had learned. The list was long. But at the same time, I didn't want to steer the conversation away from my sister's special day, so I settled on, "Don't sweat the small stuff in life. It's a waste of precious time, and time is valuable."

I knew the smiles acknowledged the lesson as the conversation returned to my sister's wedding. As they discussed the details, I realized something. For the first time since my diagnosis, I could share something about cancer, something that I had learned, without an emotional breakdown.

Am I starting to process the journey in order to heal?

Looking over at my sister, watching her be the center of attention, having all the well-deserved glory, laughing, and carrying on, I realized how far we had come. At one point, she considered postponing her wedding. Together, we went through six chemo cocktail infusions and planned the bulk of her wedding inside a chemo room. But now, as I watched her, I knew that this moment was why I fought. This was the moment I didn't want to miss. This was the *why*, and I had survived the *how*.

But that's life. It seldom goes as planned. Sometimes we fight with our last bit of energy to reach those fairy tale moments. But when they come, I can promise you this; they'll live in your memory forever. Every sacrifice leading up to it will be worth it.

SMALL VICTORIES

I KNEW EXACTLY what a mosquito bite meant.

On our honeymoon in Maui, Bruce and I had stood outside our hotel in bathing suits, mesmerized by a stunning sunset. The moment was soon interrupted by dozens of mosquitoes buzzing in my ears and landing on my arms, legs, ankles, and feet. I ran inside the hotel room for some cortisone cream and counted seven dime-sized bites while Bruce had none.

"What is it about me?" I'd grumbled, frustrated that ever since I was a child, I had to drench my skin in sticky citronella oil that smelled like chemicals anytime the weather turned humid.

But in the summer and autumn, during the chemo portion of my cancer journey, mosquitoes avoided me for the first time in my life. I could be drenched in sweat, and there was zero attraction. Occasionally, a small pink spot would appear on my skin where a mosquito started to feast, and then quickly realized the mistake. I've read articles that question whether mosquitoes sense chemo in a cancer patient's blood, but speaking from experience, they absolutely can.

Exactly two months after my final chemo, I was sitting outside in our backyard, staring at a ceiling of stars, when I felt a mosquito on my forearm. As I swatted it away multiple times, I realized that its perseverance proved that the chemo had vanished from my system.

There were also growth spurts of hair happening all over my body. My legs needed to be shaved. Armpits, too. My female parts reminded me of puberty while my nose became full of tiny, microscopic hairs. Seedlings were growing all over my head, no longer clustered in patches. My body was on the mend.

Dr. Santos wasn't intrigued when I informed him about the mosquito incident. Focused more on prescribing Tamoxifen, he instructed that I take a pill every day for five years.

"How will the drug keep cancer from coming back?" I asked.

"Your cancer is ER and PR positive since you had hormone-receptor-positive breast cancer. This medicine will attach itself to the hormone receptor if a cancer cell reappears. It will then block the estrogen from attaching to it," he told me, staring at the monitor as he sent the pharmacy the prescription.

"How effective is it?"

"It can reduce the risk of a recurrence in premenopausal women by thirty to fifty percent." I was hoping for better odds. A pill wasn't going to prevent cancer alone.

"As for side effects," Dr. Santos said, "some women experience severe hot flashes, depression, constipation, and bone pain, along with a loss of libido, dry skin, and mood swings." *Here we go again!* "The biggest concern," he added, "is that there's a slim chance you may get blood clots in your legs and lungs. The percentage is meager, about one percent, but it's something you need to be aware of."

Aren't blood clots deadly?

But then he said something promising, "Once you're done with the monoclonal antibody therapy infusions, you need to have your port removed."

Immediately, my concern about the side effects disappeared. The suggestion offered a level of confidence that I hadn't even realized I needed to hear.

"I shouldn't keep it in longer just in case?" I needed to make sure.

"It can start an infection when not in use. I feel it's best to have it removed," Dr. Santos advised.

And then I couldn't help it. I blurted out, "I'm scared the cancer will return!" Although the fear had been lurking in my mind for weeks, I was surprised to hear myself actually say it.

"Everyone tells me that. It's a common concern," he said. *Of course, every cancer patient is paranoid about a recurrence. After spending months fighting a deadly disease, the last thing you want to do is jump back in the ring to go another round.* But then he added, "Think of it this way. You have nine more infusions, twenty radiation therapies, and five years of Tamoxifen to take. Even though you won't see me as much, don't worry, you're not finished yet," and then smiled.

Again, his perspective was vastly different than mine. As a frontline soldier, I'd convinced myself the fight was over, but as the Commander, he was fortifying the city to prevent another attack.

Before ending our appointment, he said, "Be sure to go to the pharmacy to pick up your prescription."

And with that reminder, a glorious ray of independence returned. Self-sufficient and empowered, *I* was to go to the pharmacy—not my sister, not a nurse, but *me*. My compromised immune system no longer kept me from doing things for myself, by myself. It's easy to take freedom for granted, but once it's gone, you realize how much it really means.

* * *

In the pharmacy line, as I waited to pick up the Tamoxifen between a screaming baby and a woman who couldn't stop coughing, I somehow heard my phone ping from my back pocket. When I checked to see who it was, there was a text from Mae.

MAE: HOW ARE YOU FEELING?

ME: PRETTY GOOD!

MAE: ARE YOU STILL JOURNALING?

ME: YEP. DAILY.

MAE: WHEN DO YOU THINK YOU'LL STOP?

I wondered the same thing. In the beginning, I thought I'd know the exact moment in time when I'd write the final word in my journal and close the book forever. But now I realize there are not enough pens, pages, or ink to ever put it to rest.

Does the cancer journey ever end?

The answer: no. It's feeling thankful for a second chance but terrified that cancer is ever-present on the sidelines waiting for the opportune time to strike. It's feeling relieved that the physical part is mostly over, but unsure how to heal emotionally and mentally. It's understanding that a new chapter is about to begin, but the past must not be forgotten, so you don't travel down the same road that circles back. It's celebrating everything while still feeling uncertain about, well, everything. Life after cancer comes with its challenges, which before becoming cancer-free, I couldn't understand.

As I stepped up to the counter and picked up the first bottle of small white pills I'd be taking for the next five years, I concluded that the cancer journey and survivorship are more about triumphs than a finish line. Big achievements include completing six rounds of chemo. Small successes are getting out of bed and walking to the bathroom despite painful neuropathy. The simple act of standing in the pharmacy by myself, breathing in the stale air infested with germs, was a small victory that deserved to be celebrated, too. I had come so far.

THE POWER OF HOPE

OUT OF THE darkness of difficulties comes the light of possibilities.

I invited my mom to join me for my third monoclonal antibody therapy infusion. It was an opportunity for her to observe real-life superheroes and meet the oncology staff that, by then, felt like family. She had heard several stories about the chemo room, including Evelyn's ten-month hair growth and how Amy's friend used the exact words my sister had to comfort her. It was time for my mother to experience it for herself.

On our drive to the medical facility, with my mom in the passenger seat beside me, I turned down the traffic report on the radio and announced something I had kept to myself. "I want to help people through their cancer journeys, but I have no idea how."

The idea had been on my mind for a while and had gained enough momentum to finally share it. The more unknowns I uncovered through personal experience, the more knowledge I gained to help others still facing their scary unknowns. My life purpose had expanded from sharing my story in hopes of motivating women to get mammograms to the desire to assist them on their own journeys if diagnosed.

"Put it out to the Universe," my mom suggested. "It'll help you find a way." Like me, she believed in a Higher Power.

"It's complicated, though," I told her as I pulled the car into the medical building's parking structure. "I have no formal training or work experience in the oncology field to have any authority to help. All I have is my experience."

"Maybe your experience is enough," she said supportively.

* * *

"Are you ready?" I asked when we stepped up to the double doors in the oncology department, about to enter the chemo room. For me, it was somewhere around the tenth time walking through them. For her, the first, and I felt the need to preemptively foreshadow what an incredible experience she was about to have. My mother nodded as I made my silent wish.

Help me find a way to live out my life purpose.

After introducing my mother to the staff, I sat in the recliner as she sat opposite me in the visitor's chair. My mother smiles a lot, especially when she's nervous. I couldn't tell if she was happy to be there or was extremely uncomfortable. It helped that my nurse was about to travel to Canada, so she shared her itinerary while accessing my port.

Hooked up to a bag of Herceptin, we saw three women enter the room. One wore the hospital's logo on her shirt pocket. The second was in her seventies and stared down at the floor, fidgeting with the flap of her purse, and the third, a woman in her mid-forties, surveyed the room, dropped her head, and then quickly looked around again. Tucked tightly beneath her arm was an orientation binder.

The hospital employee motioned for them to stay put and

walked briskly toward us. Although I thought I knew every person in the oncology department by now, I had never seen this employee before.

"May I ask you something?" she said.

"Sure," I replied.

"Do you see those two women standing over there?" I nodded. "Would it be okay to show them your port and answer some questions?" I nodded again.

As she walked away, I glanced at my mom; her mouth gaped in disbelief. Her eyes were wide, and she wore an expression I couldn't read.

"What is it?"

"This is it. This is what you asked for in the car. It's coming to you," she said.

As I glanced back at the employee who was now talking to the two women, I realized my mom was right. Never had a wish come true so quickly. The Universe sent me the first patient to help in less than an hour.

The three women approached. "Would it be possible for you to show them your port?" the employee asked, which prompted me to pull down the collar of my shirt and showcase the implant. Moving closer to look, the two visitors studied it thoroughly.

Loosening her grip on the blue binder, the younger woman asked, "Do you like having a port?"

Before responding, the employee interrupted with, "I'll be right back," and rushed out of the room, leaving the two mothers alone with their daughters.

"Yes, I do," I replied.

"I'm Elizabeth, and this is my mom, Catherine."

"Nice to meet you," I said, taking a moment to personalize the exchange. "I'm Jennifer, and this is my mom, Mary. I know what you're dealing with. It's a lot right now."

"It's so much," she divulged. "How many rounds of chemo do you have to do? Are you still doing chemo?"

"I did six rounds, three weeks apart. I'm finished with chemo and had a lumpectomy," I told her. And then, still riding on a cancer-free high, I shared, "Nineteen days ago, I was told I was cancer-free." Both of their faces lit up when they heard the news. "I am now on the preventative side of it in the middle of my non-chemo infusions and will soon be starting radiation."

"That's incredible that you made it to the other side," Elizabeth said, her eyes bright with hope.

Catherine placed the palms of her hands together in prayer and then clapped in silent applause. "That is so wonderful that you're cancer-free," she said.

"Does it feel like it's some sort of dream?" Elizabeth asked.

"Words can't describe it," I gushed.

"Did you experience a lot of side effects during chemo?" Elizabeth had a lot of questions that needed to be answered, which I understood. She was still facing so many unknowns.

Before I could respond, her mom enthusiastically repeated, "How wonderful to be cancer-free!" While Elizabeth was focused on surviving the upcoming treatments, Catherine was focused on her daughter's survival. Her hands were still silently applauding.

With a smile, I turned my attention to Elizabeth and replied, "The side effects were severe for me, but everybody has different reactions. I met one woman who said her worst side effect was fatigue. That was my least." I didn't want to scare her, but she deserved to hear *my* truth. Regardless of which side effects I experienced, the cancer-free outcome carried the most weight.

"Do you have any advice for me?" There was an eagerness on Elizabeth's face. She needed something, anything, that I could give her to help her step onto the path of her own treatments.

"Listen to your body. Rest when needed. Drink a lot of water."

The last one came from Bruce's mom, which I felt obligated to pass on.

My mom, who had been quietly listening, said proudly, "Her recent kidney and liver tests were good. There wasn't any permanent damage caused by the chemo. She drank a lot of water, so I think that might be it."

My mother believed in drinking an abundance of water to cure anything. When I had the flu as a child, she'd say, "Drink plenty of water. Flush it out," and then she'd line up eight glasses of water on the kitchen counter. "You need to push the liquids." (Pushing the liquids means peeing a lot, but just like chemo, a lot of peeing seemed to help.)

The employee returned. "Are you ready to go?" she asked, slightly out of breath.

"Maybe I'll see you in here sometime," Elizabeth said.

"I'd like that," I replied as they turned to leave.

But instead of being slumped over, they looked up as they walked out. Their postures had changed after our conversation. I could tell by how the superheroes smiled in response that Elizabeth made eye contact with them. The change confirmed that Elizabeth and her mother were already acclimated to the room and were processing their new realities.

As soon as they left, my mom was anxious to say, "This is it, honey. This is your purpose. You gave them the most powerful gift of all."

"What's that?" I asked.

"Hope. You gave them each hope."

In search of my life purpose, destiny brought me cancer. Cancer revealed my purpose. The Universe brought me Elizabeth and Catherine to put my goal into action. It was nothing short of a heavenly miracle.

To this day, after mentoring hundreds of patients and helping to support them through their breast cancer journeys, I am continually inspired by how fortunate I am to connect weekly with real-life superheroes. It is a constant reminder that hope, much like joy, is contagious, and hope, in itself, is powerful.

EMERGING

IT WAS time to integrate back into my old life as a new me. I had become a recluse with chemo side effects and found comfort in being alone. My house was my comfort zone as it kept me away from germs. And since I had trouble mustering the energy to meet up with people or have lengthy conversations, home allowed me the space I needed to rest and heal. But the time had come to emerge.

In the regular world, most people don't change much in six months. They may have different haircuts, or their weight might fluctuate, but things pretty much stay the same. And when it comes to their happiness, or lack of it, the same problems usually exist. Their boss still micromanages, their bank account balance isn't what they want it to be, and they long for more vacation time.

But in the cancer world, things change quickly. Not just physically but mentally and emotionally. A diagnosis forces you to dissect your life to make sense of what is happening, which in turn, accelerates self-transformation and growth. And with a shifted perspective, I was unable to return to my previous life, even if I wanted to.

So much about me had changed.

Ordinary things, like common complaints, became difficult to accept. If someone said something like, "I hate how the stylist cut my hair," or, "I am exhausted from being on my feet all day," I responded with silence, wishing I had enough hair to cut and enough energy to stand for more than an hour. And so I tried to adapt to the same world I once knew, but as an entirely different person.

Now cancer-free, I started openly sharing my secret with family members, co-workers, and clients. The reactions ranged from shock to tears, and some felt the sting of rejection that I had kept this massive secret from them as if keeping it hidden was something personal against their character.

One person looked at me dumbfounded and replied, "To be honest, I feel offended you didn't tell me sooner," which was to be expected. I had already considered that those who weren't told when I was diagnosed might see that choice as a reflection of my trust in them, even though trust was never the issue.

As for THE SECRET SOCIETY, although they knew about the details of my journey, many of them hadn't seen me in person since the start of chemo. When my Aunt Marilyn flew into Palm Springs to spend Thanksgiving with my mom, Betty, Bruce, and me, I was concerned that my sudden change in appearance might make her feel uncomfortable, so I decided to keep my ball cap on *inside* our house.

After dinner, Bruce and I cleared the dishes to make room for a game of cards, another Thanksgiving tradition. As we rinsed plates and placed them in the dishwasher, Marilyn walked over and put her hand on my shoulder. Given how we'd all stuffed ourselves with turkey, cranberries, and yams, I expected her to say, "Do you have any indigestion medicine?" But instead, she said, "You look beautiful without your hat, too. With a nice-shaped head, don't feel like you need to wear it all the time," and then walked away.

I was embarrassed. She'd spotted my insecurity. I needed my cap. Or did I? *Is wearing a hat more about my own self-esteem than protecting her from my new appearance? What am I protecting her from anyway? Reality?* I realized I was pretending that everything was normal, even though it wasn't.

Unsure why I felt the need to hide the new me, I hurried into the bedroom and stared at my reflection in the mirror. As I removed the cap, I observed my hair, which was jet black and about a half-inch long in most places. Without enough weight for it to lie down, it spiked straight up.

This. Is. Me. Not the pre-cancer me, but the changed me. Before I could expect others to accept it, I had to learn to accept it myself.

I left the cap off and returned to the kitchen, hoping no one would make a remark. They all looked up but returned to what they were doing. Betty shuffled a deck of cards. My mom jotted down names on a score sheet. Bruce searched for a coaster for Marilyn's water glass. I took a seat, no longer worried about protecting anyone from anything. I wasn't who I was before, and it was okay for people to see that.

What I didn't expect was that removing my hat was freeing. Maybe not "burn my bra" liberating like in the sixties, but for me, things were progressing. I certainly wasn't ready to stop wearing my hat in public, but that moment marked a step forward. Whether I was taking baby steps or giant leaps, I was moving in the right direction.

TIME FOR AVATAR

SIX DAYS LATER, I got my first tattoo at the radiation facility in Hollywood. Actually, I got four of them at one time. They weren't cool symbols or motivational phrases, but instead, tiny black moles in permanent ink orbiting my nipple that would help to line up the machine.

Once the therapist was finished, she performed a trial run so Dr. Tanaka could study the mapping and give her the thumbs up to proceed with radiation. When the therapist said, "Head down to the basement to meet up with Joey for your orientation," I knew Dr. Tanaka had approved.

The place was packed when the elevator doors opened. In the waiting room, everyone stared intently at an electronic board on the wall as if watching a movie. It seemed the only thing missing was a concession stand selling popcorn, fizzy soda, and M&M's.

Joey graciously introduced himself. He was in his late twenties and eager to tell me about what I should and shouldn't do before and after radiation.

"You can bathe regularly but do not use washcloths, sponges, or loofahs in the radiated area since your skin will be sensitive and fragile. Place the soap in the palm of your hand and gently dab the area clean," he said, demonstrating the *dabbing* action on his forearm. It was the same method that I used to protect my hair during chemotherapy.

But before he could continue, we were both distracted by a woman who leaped out of her chair and hurried down the adjacent hallway. After a few seconds, Joey turned his attention back to me.

"Apply aloe vera to the affected skin three times a day, but wait until after your treatment to apply it. Arrive here with clean skin. Avoid body creams, powders, perfumes, and lotions, and never use heating pads, especially electric blankets."

"What about deodorant?" I asked.

"You can wear it after treatment, but not before. Be sure to read the labels and only use aluminum-free deodorant. Avoid shaving your right armpit area. Wear loose-fitting clothing, no underwire bras, and avoid A, C, and E supplements. Any other questions?"

"What's up with that digital board on the wall?"

"A patient's name appears next to the assigned room when it's their turn to go in."

I glanced up at the screen to see the list of rooms that had been named after blockbuster hits: *Rocky, James Bond, Braveheart, Gladiator,* and *Avatar,* to name a few. I chuckled at the thought that the radiation facility in Hollywood is *so* Hollywood.

"Which room will I be in?" I asked, curious to know if I had seen the movie and, better yet, if I liked it.

He glanced down at a sheet of paper. "*Avatar,*" he said.

In 2010, *Avatar* won Oscars for Best Art Direction, Best Cinematography, and Best Visual Effects, so if it could win me over for being the best room for radiation, I figured I may have won an award myself.

"What time should I arrive each day?" I asked. *Please let it be before or after rush-hour traffic,* I thought.

"You have the 7:20 a.m. time slot, so—" but he was inter-rupted by three loud strikes of a bell. After the third strike, the entire room clapped and cheered. He waited for the noise to stop before continuing, "Please arrive fifteen minutes before your appointment. This place operates on a tight schedule."

"Did someone finish their last treatment?" I asked, intrigued.

"Yes. A bell hangs on the wall in the nurse's station. It's tradi-tion to ring it after the final therapy."

Hoping it wasn't a requirement, I asked, "Does everyone have to do it?" I preferred to celebrate in my own way … by eating another giant calzone with my sister.

"No, but you should," he said with an enticing grin. "You'll start on Monday, December fourth, and your last therapy will land on January second since you'll have Christmas Day and New Year's Day off."

After the orientation was finished, Joey left, but I sat there for a few minutes longer in the waiting area. By the beginning of the new year, radiation would be finished. For 186 days, I was caught between a diagnosis and becoming cancer-free. As the year was coming to a close, I was happy to put it behind me.

Time is tricky. During challenging times, it trudges along despite our desire to speed it up. During the good times, it passes quickly, and we want to slow it down. So often, we wish we could go back and change things or skip forward to know what's in store. And sometimes, when everything aligns, we hold onto the present, hoping that circumstances don't change. But time respects none of that. There are no bad years or good years, just years of time filled with unforeseen experiences, moments of clar-ity, growth, learned lessons, and surprises, and we must accept that this "adventure" is what life is all about.

"Life isn't for the weak," my mother-in-law always says.

It certainly isn't. Life is what makes us stronger, and the longer we live, the stronger we become.

THE LETTER

To HEAL, I had to acknowledge and fully accept everything I had been through, including the painful parts.

Our under-dressed Christmas tree stood in the corner of the living room, wrapped in a string of stark white lights. As I reached into the plastic bin of decorations, I saw a small frame with an old black and white photo of my Uncle Don in his army uniform.

Years earlier, I had decided to decorate our tree with family photos, from baby portraits to wedding pictures. At that time, all the people in the pictures, except my Grandma Wells, were alive. But a decade later, some of the people in the photos had passed, leaving only a memory in their place. It was a haunting reminder, especially this year, of how fragile and fleeting life is.

Everything about this Christmas feels different.

Before cancer, I'd pretty much rushed through the holiday season, stressed and complaining. Everything felt like an obligation, a task to be checked off a list, so I could finally relax when finished. But for the first time in 42 years, I discovered the miracle of Christmas: that being alive for Christmas was a miracle in itself.

Where do real-life superheroes spend their holidays? Thinking about the chemo room, I knew not everyone could celebrate the holidays the way they wanted to. With compromised immune systems, some may not be able to travel or have family over. A bite of a Christmas cake might spike a bout of nausea. Neuropathy makes wrapping presents difficult, if not impossible. Some people will be isolated and alone, sleeping off depression. There will be people recently diagnosed who find it hard to enjoy the sights and sounds of the season as they embark on one of the most challenging journeys of their lives. Others will be told their cancers are terminal and struggle with how to break the news to their families. While healthy people take vacations from work or go on holiday breaks, cancer patients cannot leave a diagnosis behind. The disease is with them in every thought and action. There's no time off from cancer.

Once I finished decorating the tree, I was inspired to write. I curled up on the sofa, tucked my feet under me, and picked up my journal. But before writing an entry documenting my day, I decided to write a letter instead.

There were so many things I wanted to tell Amy on her first chemo day, to comfort her when she asked, "Why me?" Unfortunately, I couldn't utter a word without becoming emotional, so I stayed quiet. Although I had healed enough to show Elizabeth and her mother my port and answer questions about side effects, there were so many more things I needed to say about cancer, life, and how one tiny malignant cell changed my entire world forever. In the letter, I could explain everything I had wanted to tell them and why I hadn't been able to speak without emotionally breaking down. By writing it, I hoped it would also further my healing.

And so, I wrote:

Dear Superhero Human,

To you, wherever you reside and wherever you are in your courageous journey.

For the holidays this year, I wish you no longer ask the Universe, "Why me?" I know how it feels to search desperately for a reason to rationalize such ruin. I hope you find the answers you seek, and they come to you as needed.

I wish that you are no longer consumed with fear. Your soul finds peace within restless nights, and you dream about a bright future instead.

I wish that your spirit becomes resilient to depression. With every step forward, I hope you gain insight and perspective. Remember that beyond the heavy sky of darkness, a sun exists. Even when it's not visible, it's there, so look for the sun in every situation.

I wish that you trust your instincts. While standing at a crossroads, unsure of which difficult decision you should make or which path to take, remember your intuition is your most valuable compass.

I wish that when you no longer recognize your reflection in the mirror, you can see how beautiful you truly are. Be proud of your tremendous strength and who you have become.

I wish that you disregard the looks of pity. Please don't base your self-esteem on other people's fear. To smile is empowering.

I wish that when you feel broken and defeated, you remember the flame of courage is still there. It waits and will ignite when needed.

I wish that you will fully embrace the journey. Destiny has given you this journey for a reason. Keep the faith as you move forward.

I wish that you remember you are not alone. When you feel isolated, remind yourself that we stand together in solidarity. We fight with you. We fight for you.

And my last wish is that you find confidence in knowing that

YOUR SPIRIT IS MORE SIGNIFICANT THAN YOUR PHYSICAL BEING. BEYOND PHYSICAL PAIN AND ILLNESS, THE "YOU" HOLDS INFINITE POWER. IT'S YOUR POWER. CANCER MAY BE CHALLENGING, BUT THE "YOU" IS MUCH TOUGHER. IT IS THE WARRIOR SPIRIT INSIDE EACH OF US.

I AM SENDING TREMENDOUS LOVE AND LIGHT TO THOSE WHO NEED IT THIS HOLIDAY SEASON.

LOVE,

JENNIFER

As I set my pen down, I felt relief knowing that more truths were set free. By acknowledging my truths and releasing them back into the Universe, they were ready for the next person who needed them. And to the person who set their truths free so I could grasp them during my journey, I'm forever grateful for your wisdom.

LAST UNKNOWN, KNOWN

At 7:20 a.m. on December 4, it was time to get zapped. *I'm Avatar-ready,* I thought. *Let's do this.*

It had been 40 days since my lumpectomy, and even though my armpit area still felt tight, I could place my right bicep up to my ear without cheating. So when my name appeared on the waiting room's electronic board, with *Avatar* next to it, I headed down the adjacent hallway to change into a gown.

"Are you Jennifer?" A therapist greeted me. I nodded. "What's the month and year you were born?" I told him, waiting in antici-pation for him to shout, "Radiation check!" But he didn't. Obvi-ously, the chemo room's protocols were quite different than the radiation room's.

And, of course, when I entered the *Avatar* room, it wasn't inhabited by the blue-skinned giants depicted in the movie (although that would have been kind of cool), but instead, a high-tech linear accelerator machine. The room that framed the machine was impressive, with recessed lighting dialed down to dusk and built-in speakers playing classical music.

This machine is going to zap me into a cancer-free future, I thought, as the therapist helped me onto the machine's platform. He stretched my right arm back, tucked a cylinder pillow beneath my knees to prevent any movement, and located my four chest tattoos to properly line up the machine.

"Hold still," he told me after I was in position. "I'll be observing from the monitor outside," he said as he left.

The machine's arm, consisting of several metal keys sandwiched inside a glass plate like the belly of a piano, hovered over me. The keys began to press down at different times, and seconds later, the arm lowered, and more keys were played. When they were all released, I heard his footsteps as he entered the room.

"You're done," the therapist said and helped me off the table.

"That's it?" I asked.

"That's it."

"I didn't feel anything," I told him, surprised. "When do you think I'll experience side effects?"

"Might be a couple of weeks. Since the same area is radiated each day, it will begin to accumulate." I knew all too well about accumulating side effects. "Be sure to apply aloe vera three times a day, even if you're not experiencing any skin issues or discomfort," he added.

"See you tomorrow," I said.

"Yep, see you tomorrow."

And that was it. My last unknown was known.

* * *

A routine quickly took shape, especially since I had to be radiated five days a week at the same time each morning. I'd leave the house in the dark, arrive early, stop for coffee, and with the scent of roasted arabica beans wafting from my cup, I'd enter the brashly-lit parking structure where I'd park and wait, filling the time by writing in my journal.

Once I checked in with the receptionist, I'd ride the elevator to the basement and find a seat in the third section of the waiting room. For whatever reason, I always chose the same seat in the same section. Given the freedom to *choose*, it's funny how we often *choose* the exact same thing.

On Friday, the morning of my fifth therapy, a woman entered and took the open chair right next to me despite the number of other empty seats further away. I could feel her nervous energy, so I steered my focus to the electronic board and prayed for my name to appear. Out of my peripheral vision, I saw the camera app was open and ready on her mobile phone as she held her arm in position to take a photo of the screen.

And then, without making eye contact, she said, "I am going to take a photo of my husband's name when it appears on the board." Her eyes were still fixated on the screen. "I'm so proud of him, and I am journaling his experience." Her mention of journaling piqued my interest. We had something in common. "I am Paige, and my husband is Bobby. He will be out of the restroom shortly, and you can meet him." I told her my name and saw the top of a man's head over the partitioned wall as she yelled out, "Bobby! Over here!" With only a few people in the room at that time of day, it was impossible for him not to see us. He'd barely arrived when his name appeared on the board next to *Gladiator*, and Paige snapped numerous photos.

My name also appeared. "I have to go," I told her. "It was nice meeting you."

"Good luck," I heard her say as her finger kept tapping the button, capturing one image after another.

On my way out, I scanned the same section of the waiting room for Paige, but she was no longer there. In her seat was a man reading a newspaper. Next to him was an older lady in a wheelchair. An eccentric woman with wide-rimmed glasses sat in the seat I'd occupied, and there was a couple dressed in nice-looking outfits while the wife knitted a scarf. The room had filled up with more people waiting for their turn to get zapped.

After completing my first week of radiation, I returned to Palm Springs to spend the weekend with Bruce and Stella.

Five therapies down, 15 to go.

THE RADIATION CLUB

After my seventh radiation therapy, I was alone in the elevator heading up to the oncology department for my fourth monoclonal antibody therapy infusion, when tears suddenly filled my eyes. I felt strangely sentimental. Maybe it was the rush of hormones pumping through me, but I experienced intense gratitude toward the cancer journey itself for the first time.

Having cancer, I was forced to dive deep within myself. Things I'd taken for granted had become appreciated. Old habits were abandoned, and new ones were considered. I experienced love like I never had before. Through my diagnosis, I found the purpose and meaning of my life. For all of those things, I was grateful. Without cancer, I wouldn't be who I am today, and there is no doubt I am a better—*and stronger*—person because of it.

And then, the following morning, back in Hollywood for radiation, I checked in and took a seat in my usual section of the waiting room. Unlike the chemo room, where it is unusual to see the same person twice since schedules are vastly different, in the radiation area, it's common. To see the same familiar faces, waiting to be zapped, even without conversation, was comforting.

But on this particular day, the eccentric woman in her mid-sixties, whom I'd noticed the day I was looking for Bobby and Paige, was sitting two chairs away and, out of nowhere, broke the silence. "I am staying at my brother's apartment since he's away on business," she announced to the rest of us. "He lives like a pig!" Everyone in our section laughed, causing her to grin and the bottom of her large-rimmed Elton John-style glasses to become buried in her cheeks. "I'm Jelsma," she said. And just like that, the rest of us introduced ourselves.

In addition to Jelsma, the group included Henry, Mr. and Mrs. Garza, Margaret, Shirley, Jules (Shirley's grown granddaughter), Joseph, Anjelica, Kindra (Anjelica's mother), and of course, Paige and Bobby.

Jelsma had undergone a double-mastectomy seven years prior, and I was surprised by her ability to turn the loss into a joke. "Look at my chest," she told the group, pointing to her white T-shirt that dropped straight down along her stomach, "it's as flat as a pancake!" Everyone laughed at her comedic delivery. Even during the worst hardships, Jelsma could extract humor and playfulness, which I respected.

I also learned a lot from meeting Henry. Although a cancer diagnosis might change a person, it doesn't have to darken one's quirkiness.

"Your name came up on the screen," I told him. (When someone was too distracted or engaged in conversation, we would let each other know.)

As a film editor, he loved to interject movie lines into conversations, so he replied, "All right, Mr. DeMille, I'm ready for my close-up," a line from *Sunset Boulevard* that he deemed appropriate.

The following week, Henry shared some devastating news with us. "My doctor told me that even with radiation to control cancer, I will only live for another ten years." At 51, the defeat in his voice was evident. We were all Henry, and the loss of hope that he would not beat his cancer, took our own hopes down a notch, too. We did our best to offer support.

"There will probably be a cure for prostate cancer by then," I told him, something I truly believed.

After a few seconds of group silence, Henry's dynamic personality powered through the darkness. "I feel the need—the need for speed," another movie line, this time from *Top Gun,* which made us all chuckle.

Although everyone was closely connected, some of us shared stronger bonds. Henry and Mr. Garza had prostate cancer, just like Margaret and I shared a breast cancer diagnosis.

"How many times have you had breast cancer?" Margaret asked me one morning.

"Once," I said, "but I am terrified it will come back. How about you?"

"This is my second time," she replied, tilting her head in a way that caused her thin braids to sway back and forth. "Although, I was fortunate to avoid chemo both times." Her comment made me wonder if she thought chemo was worse than having a recurrence.

I mentioned, "According to a few online searches, the definition of remission states that it's a temporary or permanent decrease of disease. Although it states that it *can* be permanent, I usually focus on the other word: *temporary.*"

Uneasy, she shifted in her chair. "That's not good."

"So, in order to create my own definition, I made up an acronym based on the letters."

"And? What is it?"

Like Henry, who can instantly recall the movie lines he's committed to memory, I announced, "Remember, every moment is special, significant, and intertwined. Own the now."

"I like that," she said, satisfied with the new definition.

And when it comes to processing trauma or not processing it, a story Jelsma told me stands out. "My sister-in-law, a breast cancer survivor, refused to talk about her experience with me when I was diagnosed. She had safely tucked it away, never to be thought of again. Then, years later, while in a movie theater watching a film with lots of medical scenes, she panicked. Unable to breathe, she collapsed on the floor, and an ambulance was called. The emergency room doctor told the family she had experienced a panic attack and should start seeing a psychologist for her PTSD."

I didn't know cancer survivors could be diagnosed with Post Traumatic Stress Disorder. It confirmed that I needed to process everything I went through because if I didn't, it'd one day reappear and force me to process it anyway (hopefully, not in a movie theater).

And I also realized that once the physical part of the cancer journey is over, the scars remain forever. For eighteen-year-old Anjelica, now partially deaf from the removal of a cancerous polyp in her ear, life substantially changed. Same with Joseph, who uses an electrolarynx ever since the operation that removed his cancer-riddled voice box.

But even when cancer robs you of physical attributes, it can't steal your sense of humor. Although Joseph didn't speak much, on occasion, he'd tell one of us on our way to get zapped, "May - the - force - be - with - you," in a robotic voice, which made us hold our stomachs from laughing so hard. Henry always laughed the hardest, which is why I think Joseph did it.

"They are the rowdy ones," a random woman said in an intentionally loud voice to her husband as she walked past our little pod of chairs in disgust.

But her insult was a compliment to us. The group thrived on the idea that we could add positive energy to the waiting room and that even though cancer is damn depressing, it couldn't take us down.

As the leader, Jelsma stood up and proudly announced, "Friends, we are *The Radiation Club*," giving our group an official name.

We weren't elite or selective in extending membership to others. Anyone was able to join if there was an empty seat in our pod. With only 12 available chairs, the membership was capped until Shirley, in a wheelchair, rolled up beside Margaret, and we gained our thirteenth member.

While Anjelica, at 18, was the youngest, Shirley, who was 88, was the oldest. "If I can beat brain cancer once, I can do it again," she said with tenacity.

Like me, Shirley had learned who and what drove her to fight. While I wanted more moments with my loved ones, she did, too. It confirmed that the warrior spirit is ageless and unstoppable.

"My honey pie is walking," she would tell us as she passed around a picture of her great-grandson. "My honey pie loves raspberries. My honey pie's new favorite toy is a firetruck." Little did the toddler know that his existence was instrumental to Shirley's survival.

And yet, for the caregivers in the group, I could see the pride they felt for their loved ones, interlocked with anxiety, fear, and sadness. Kindra, Anjelica's mother, would look up at the ceiling with tears in her eyes when she said, "When Anjelica was diagnosed with cancer..." and I could see it in the way Paige still snapped pictures of Bobby's name on the board.

But through all the cancer-related craziness, what I loved most about *The Radiation Club* was how normal we felt around each other and how open we all were. There wasn't a single look of pity. Conversations about cancer, or even death, weren't taboo. We minimized cancer's power by talking about it in casual conversations, with regular voices instead of whispers. And often, we skipped over the cancer talk entirely and focused on other topics like good mechanics in the area, vintage shops, or our weekend plans. Cancer was just one topic of many. Together, we were a force that cancer couldn't dominate and control.

I can't fully define the dynamic between us or why, in a huge room of quiet patients, the thirteen of us seemed to gravitate to each other. When we were together, we embodied an energy that others didn't. Our bond was so apparent; it was as if we had known one another for ages. A reunion from a past life that we didn't know existed.

And although I would have never sought out a support group, a group of support formed around me. Life is hard, but less so when going through the brunt of it together. Seeing my new friends each morning made the cancer journey—*even though it seems crazy to admit*—enjoyable.

Unexpected friendship was another valuable gift I received from having cancer.

THE REAL SANTA

EVERYTHING ABOUT CANCER IS PERSONAL: how a person reacts to the news, when they share it, why they got it, how they treat it, and whether or not they come to terms with the experience. Each one of us is unique.

A breast cancer survivor I mentor recently told me, "Since I had surgery without radiation or chemo, I often feel like my story isn't significant. My diagnosis feels like a big deal to me, but I feel embarrassed saying it was when other people have it worse."

"It *is* a big deal. It's *your* journey, and that's all that matters," I reminded her.

Cancer is not a competition. We shouldn't judge a person's situation based on their level of suffering, at which stage they discovered it, or which body part it invaded. The only thing that matters is how we each embrace the journey—or any difficult journey—for that matter.

On December 22, after my fifteenth zap, the nurse guided me down a hallway into a different room for a skin evaluation by an on-site doctor. His approval was required in order to move forward with the last five targeted boosts.

"It looks like an average sunburn," he told me after examining the radiated area. "Does it hurt?"

"Stings but doesn't hurt," I told him, happy that there wasn't any blistering, even though the burn had worsened from an accumulation of zaps.

"I'll sign off for you to proceed. And the good news is, the rest of your skin will begin to heal since the boosts will only affect the section of skin where the cancer was removed."

Dressed in my favorite pair of jeans, a wool sweater, and of course, my ball cap, I met Jelsma in the hallway. She wore a furry Santa hat and held a white felt stocking in her arms. When she saw me, she plunged her hand into the stocking and pulled out a shiny gold box, which she placed in my palm.

"Merry Christmas," she told me and then added, "It's a dark chocolate truffle."

I wrapped my fingers around the gift and held it to my heart. "I love it. Thank you."

"We've come a long way, kid," she said, grabbing me and giving me the type of hug that permeates every cell of your being with love.

As a child, on Christmas Eve, I'd always leave a handwritten list of questions for Santa next to a plate of holiday cookies in hopes he'd answer them while indulging.

The questions were childish but specific:

WHO IS YOUR FAVORITE REINDEER?

WHAT IS YOUR FAVORITE COLOR?

WHEN IS YOUR BIRTHDAY?

DO YOU LIKE LIVING IN THE NORTH POLE?

DO THE ELVES GET IN FIGHTS?

On Christmas morning, I'd rush downstairs to check for answers. *Nothing.* Disappointed, I'd ask my dad, "Why didn't Santa answer me?" Offended, I thought, *Santa certainly liked the cookies.*

My dad would chuckle, giving some lame excuse like, "He's probably too busy delivering packages." I couldn't see the humor in the situation like my father did.

Sometimes, I'd try to catch Santa. I'd wait for him on the flight of stairs, hoping to witness him pulling packages out of his burlap sack. Eventually, I'd become bored and tired, crawling back up the steps to go to bed in defeat.

In the morning, I'd search for mishaps, things he accidentally left behind like dirty boot prints on the carpet, a fallen strand of beard hair, or the lingering smell of pipe smoke. But the only scent was my mother's evergreen candle on the coffee table, leaving me bummed that Santa had been there, but I had missed him once again.

What I couldn't have predicted was that one day, I'd meet a real-life Santa. And when I did, it wouldn't be a robust "he" but an average-sized "she." Instead of living at the North Pole, she resided in a single-story stucco in the San Fernando Valley. Instead of a sleigh, she rode around town in a 2010 Buick with leather seats cracked from the sun's heat. And I wouldn't meet the real-life Santa in my living room or at the mall but at a radiation facility in Hollywood. Even though I had no clue if the elves fought or which reindeer she preferred, I knew her birthday was in September; she loved wearing white and had no issue making jokes about the double mastectomy she'd had seven years prior.

Sometimes the greatest gifts aren't the ones found in perfectly wrapped boxes but the hugs you get from people who make you feel great. It costs nothing but means everything. As I walked away, I knew I'd miss the mornings I spent with *The Radiation Club,* and a piece of me didn't want it to be over.

CHRISTMAS

"THE BALL CAP looks ridiculous with my cocktail dress," I lamented to Bruce on Christmas Eve.

But there wasn't time to go find a fancier alternative. In less than an hour, we would lose our reservation if we didn't make it to Miro's in time. Besides that, we still needed to pick up Betty.

"Don't worry," Bruce said as he straightened his tie. "You'll look beautiful without it."

I knew he was trying to assuage my doubts and build my confidence, but the cap had become a disguise I could hide behind. It had been liberating taking it off on Thanksgiving around family, but to step out into society and subject myself to more looks of pity, still made me feel incredibly vulnerable.

My mind raced for alternatives. Lady Wig was still crammed in the back of my closet. *There's no way I'm wearing that.* Although the bin of scarves sat on the top shelf, I cringed at the thought. I opened every drawer but found nothing. Disappointed for not being proactive and prepared, I sat down on the edge of our bed, crushed by my anxiety.

"If we don't leave now," Bruce warned, "we'll miss our reservation." I glanced at the clock, already knowing he was right.

"Damn," I muttered and threw the ball cap onto the bed.

I practically ran to our parked car in the driveway in my two-inch heels. It was one thing for total strangers to stare at me, people I'd never see again, but if one of our neighbors inquired, I'd have to stop and spend time explaining. I just wanted to enjoy the evening at a nice restaurant and not tell people how I'd spent the past year fighting cancer. I looked around, relieved that the street was empty and quiet; our neighbors were involved in their own holiday gatherings.

As I waited for Bruce to unlock the car door, a gust of wind blew by, rattling the mailbox, swirling up sand, and shuffling through every strand of hair on my head. As the wind shifted directions, so did my hair.

I latched onto the soft pulling sensation. There was a movement happening on the top of my head. Free from the confines of my hat, my new strands of hair moved in synchronicity, causing goose bumps to form on my arms and legs.

This is what it feels like to have hair. What an incredible feeling.

"Let's go," Bruce said as he unlocked the passenger door and started the engine.

With no time to spare, we picked up Bruce's mom and pulled up to the valet a few minutes late. I rushed through the front door to ensure that they hadn't given our reservation away.

"James," I told the host. As he searched through a book with a long list of names, I scanned the restaurant, expecting stares from other patrons and the pity looks that always seemed to follow. But on Christmas Eve, everyone was preoccupied with eating, drinking, and laughing. A waiter glanced over briefly but then turned his attention back to the tray of cocktails he was carrying without so much as a raised eyebrow.

"Ah yes," the host finally said, grabbing three leather-bound menus. And without his eyes wandering to the top of my head, he said, "Follow me."

When a young woman brought us water, she didn't look at me longer than at Betty or Bruce. When the waiter told us about the dinner specials, instead of his gaze drifting up to my uncommon hairdo, his eyes remained focused on mine. There wasn't a single look of pity or sadness about my condition. Despite the length of my hair, my appearance had returned to normal, as if I wasn't a cancer patient any longer.

It felt miraculous to be one of the crowd.

My high school art teacher always said, "Be anything but normal." I took her words to heart when I'd go to thrift stores to buy crazy clothes. The weirder I looked, the cooler I felt. But through my cancer journey, I realized that normal is only boring to those who *are* normal. When cancer changes your appearance, blending in feels incredible.

* * *

At my mother's house on Christmas Day, we toasted to "health and happiness" before indulging in our traditional holiday brunch of ham, eggs, and homemade cinnamon rolls. With my appetite back, I over-ate without regret.

Two hours later, when the floor was covered with crumpled gift wrap and Burl Ives was singing Christmas carols on replay, I looked around the living room, remembering the day I told my mom and sister about my diagnosis. At that time, I wondered if I'd make it to December. But as I sat in an armchair, watching my sister organize her gifts, my mom excited about a new perfume, Bruce holding Stella, and David integrating seamlessly into our family, it felt surreal but fantastic.

When life gets derailed, the simplest things tend to provide the most comfort. They are beautifully predictable and stable when life itself, isn't. And that's when you realize there's something extraordinary in the ordinary, to feel normal is a blessing, and that the things we often take for granted should be embraced and celebrated.

That Christmas, normalcy never felt so good.

CANCER NARRATIVE

I ANNOUNCED to *The Radiation Club* that I had changed my mind about ringing the bell. "Tomorrow, I'll do it. After my twentieth zap."

Arthur looked up from his newspaper, surprised by the sudden change. "Are - you - sure - you - are - going - to - do - it?"

"I am," I confirmed, no longer concerned about being a spectacle when surrounded by such incredible friends.

As soon as Bobby got up for treatment, Paige jumped out of her seat to sit next to me. For the first time, she didn't take photos of Bobby's name on the screen, which meant something was wrong. I could see on her face that the stress of being a caregiver had taken its toll.

"I don't know how he really feels," she said, worried. "After chemo, he says he's okay, but I know he's not. Since you did chemo, I thought maybe you could help me understand." Bobby's treatment plan combined chemo and radiation to combat his throat cancer.

"I'm sure he doesn't want to stress you out more than you

already are. If he's quiet or doesn't want to elaborate, just know that he's doing it out of love to protect you," I told her, which is why I often used fewer words when communicating with my loved ones.

"I hadn't considered that he might keep it from me out of love." As she sat there taking in what I had told her, I could tell more things were on her mind. "He won't eat and is losing so much weight." We'd all noticed how frail Bobby had become, but knowing how the "Chemo Diet" works, I was confident that he'd begin to bulk up once he finished chemotherapy.

"Ask him what food he craves each day," I told her as she paid close attention. "It doesn't matter if it's healthy. Whatever he tells you, try and get it for him. The important thing is that he eats *something*."

"He does like chocolate milkshakes," she said. And then, after another minute of silence, she said, "Oh, and Bobby told me that it's rude to ask people what type of cancer they have. Is that true?"

It was a good question. One of those implied rules, even though there isn't an official "how to" book on the etiquette of speaking about cancer.

"He's right," I told her. "If patients offer the information, they are open to discussing it. But if they don't, respect their privacy. If they want to tell you, they will."

Paige threw her arms around me. "I feel like I understand my husband better," she told me with overwhelming appreciation.

I was happy to help provide the information she craved, but at the same time, I highlighted a bigger problem. To beat cancer on all fronts, we must come together to change the narrative surrounding the disease. Caregivers need to be able to ask questions. I could tell Paige had put considerable thought into who she could ask her questions, and if we hadn't all formed the bond we did through *The Radiation Club*, she may not have known who to ask or asked anyone at all.

290

Patients, even when feeling sick or tired, must be honest and speak out about what they are going through (even though I was often guilty of keeping it to myself). It's difficult for their caregivers to know the right things to say, when to give them space, or when to show tough love. Patients must help caregivers understand the care they need, even if they think it will cause their loved ones to worry more. Believe me, the caregivers will still be worried regardless of what the patient says, so not telling them doesn't spare them any pain.

Society must understand that their reactions matter. How they react to a person's diagnosis or a patient's appearance, matters. And most importantly, instead of jumping to the conclusion that cancer automatically leads to death, we must focus on statistics. There are over 17 million cancer survivors in the United States alone, and the number is projected to increase. And even though the topic is taboo, uncomfortable, and difficult to discuss, the reality that so many people survive cancer, and continue to thrive afterward, shouldn't be overlooked. Just because they see someone bald and gaunt from chemotherapy does not mean that person is about to die. What that person needs most is encouragement and support, not looks of pity.

And last, we must all take some responsibility in doing what we can to prevent cancer in our bodies. Self-exams, routine wellness checks, and maintaining a lifestyle with exercise and a healthy diet are all things we have control over and aid in the early detection and prevention of cancer. To take back control of the disease, we must do everything in our power to stop it.

Let's face it, challenging circumstances require challenging conversations. But through honesty and heartfelt interactions, we not only gain insight and grow as individuals, but we are able to grow as a society. And I truly believe that we can overcome anything, united as one.

As I walked into the *Avatar* room for my nineteenth zap, I

wished the machine could zap us all into a cancer-free future. Maybe someday. But for now, I had to be more open with sharing my own cancer story in hopes that, if I am lucky, it might make a difference.

For me, this memoir is my beginning.

RING THE BELL

On January 2, after ringing in the new year, I was ready to ring the bell. I was excited to introduce *The Radiation Club* to my sister and have her join me for my final session festivities. I checked in with the receptionist, and we rode the elevator down to the basement for the last time. We weren't there long before I saw my name appear next to *Avatar,* which felt like the closing credits to a physical journey that, at one time, seemed would never end.

After being zapped, I got dressed and walked down the hallway, motioning for my sister and *The Radiation Club* to join me in the nurse's station. As we squeezed into the small office, I stood in front of the bronze plaque that hung on the wall. With a bell attached, I read the inscription out loud:

"RING THIS BELL,
THREE TIMES WELL,
ITS TOLL TO CLEARLY SAY,
MY TREATMENT'S DONE,
THIS COURSE IS RUN,
AND I AM ON MY WAY!"

Yanking on the cord, I rang the bell three times. With each

clank, tears filled my eyes. Shirley rolled up in her wheelchair, and I leaned down for a hug. Joseph had a smile that I swore could bring angels down from heaven. Mr. Garcia, wearing the red scarf we had watched Mrs. Garcia knit, congratulated me and squeezed my hand.

Henry recited, "The stuff that dreams are made of!" It was another movie line, this time from *The Maltese Falcon*.

Margaret rested her head on my shoulder, her little braids tickling my cheek. Anjelica and her mom clapped in unison as I joined Paige and Bobby in a group hug.

It felt like the perfect finale to such a crazy, cancer-fighting journey—at least the physical aspect of it. After seven more non-chemo infusions and a couple of MUGA heart scans, my port would finally be removed. The hardest part of the physical journey was over. It was time. Time to fully process the emotional and mental ramifications of a diagnosis.

On our way out, Jelsma stopped us, handing me a sheet of paper with a pen. "Write down your contact information. We all need to stay in touch." I scribbled down my email and phone number, hoping for a *Radiation Club* reunion.

I held my sister's hand as we rode the elevator back up to the ground level and exited the radiation facility for the last time. As we stepped out into the unseasonably warm January sun, I told her what I'd been waiting so many months to say.

"I kicked cancer's ass. We did it together."

And her smile, proved, we had.

THE FINAL JOURNAL ENTRY

"EVERY WORTHWHILE ACCOMPLISHMENT, BIG OR LITTLE, HAS ITS STAGES
OF DRUDGERY AND TRIUMPH; A BEGINNING, A STRUGGLE, AND A VICTORY."
— MAHATMA GANDHI

The physical part of the cancer journey, the scariest part, had
ended, and I no longer felt the desire to document my daily
thoughts. I knew that the emotional and mental aspects of my
diagnosis would continue on, maybe even forever. It was time to
stop writing in my journal and move forward with a new normal.

Often, I think back to the Italian restaurant in Westlake
Village, where we sat celebrating my sister's newly-purchased
wedding gown. Over lunch, Daya asked me, "So, what is the
biggest thing you learned from having cancer?" Although there
were too many takeaways to mention at the time, I decided to list
them all for my final entry.

Here is what I learned during those 247 days from the time I
was diagnosed to the time I rang the closing bell:

- LIKE I TOLD DAYA, "DON'T SWEAT THE SMALL STUFF IN LIFE.
  IT'S A WASTE OF PRECIOUS TIME, AND TIME IS VALUABLE."

- BODIES IN MOTION STAY IN MOTION. KEEP MOVING.

- FIND THE TIME TO MEDITATE. THE ANSWERS TO LIFE'S MOST COMPLICATED QUESTIONS WILL OFTEN SURFACE WHEN YOUR MIND IS STILL AND READY TO ACCEPT THEM.

- WHEN YOU WAKE UP IN THE MORNING OR BEFORE BED, LIST FIVE THINGS YOU ARE GRATEFUL FOR.

- WHAT YOU CONSUME, YOU BECOME. SO BE CONSCIOUS OF WHAT YOU EAT, DRINK, AND LISTEN TO.

- WATER CLEARS THE TOXINS AWAY. DRINK LOTS OF IT. (YES, MOM, YOU WERE RIGHT.)

- LAUGHTER IS THERAPY. WATCH FUNNY MOVIES. BE GOOFY. NOTHING IN LIFE IS **THAT** SERIOUS.

- STAY IN THE PRESENT IF YOU WANT TO EXPERIENCE HAPPINESS.

- MY GRANDPA WELLS ALWAYS SAID, "DON'T JUDGE A PERSON UNTIL YOU'VE WALKED THREE DAYS IN HIS SHOES." REMEMBER THAT WE ARE ALL ON OUR OWN JOURNEYS. DON'T COMPARE YOUR JOURNEY TO ANYONE ELSE'S.

- LIFE IS DIFFICULT. BUT WHEN IT'S TOO MUCH, REMEMBER, COURAGE WILL RISE. IT'S YOUR POWER. THE FIRE TO OVERCOME WILL ALWAYS IGNITE.

- STOP WORRYING ABOUT WHAT MAY OR MAY NOT HAPPEN. IT WILL NOT CHANGE THE OUTCOME. WHAT IS SUPPOSED TO BE WILL BE.

- Own up to mistakes in order to move forward.

- It's not your responsibility to change someone. Live out your truth but listen to theirs with compassion.

- You are unique—a masterpiece.

- Material wealth provides stability and comfort but can never provide lasting happiness. Only moments with loved ones can fill that space in your heart.

- Surround yourself with people who bring you joy. Be the joy to others.

- Smile. When it feels impossible to find a reason to smile, remember how lucky you are to be alive to watch another sunrise and sunset. You are truly blessed.

- Do not waste your energy trying to control things. You'll only become exhausted.

- Let things move through you; feel the freedom in moving along with it. This is the flow of life.

- Everyone is facing challenges. Be kind.

- Choose your internal words wisely. Make sure the inner voice you hear is nurturing and loving. Yes, you are beautiful. Yes, you are strong. Yes, you are enough.

- EVERY PERSON YOU MEET SERVES A PURPOSE IN YOUR LIFE. SOME ARE MEANT TO STAY. SOME WILL REMAIN STRANGERS. SOME YOU WILL LEARN FROM. SOME YOU WILL TEACH.

- WORDS ARE POWERFUL. CHOOSE THEM WISELY. IT'S OKAY TO WALK AWAY WHEN YOU'RE UPSET. ONCE THE EMOTIONS HAVE SUBSIDED, APPROACH THE SITUATION WITH CALMNESS AND A CLEAR PERSPECTIVE.

- OWN YOUR EXISTENCE. YOU ARE EXACTLY WHERE YOU'RE SUPPOSED TO BE IN LIFE.

- THE SMALLEST THINGS OFTEN HOLD TREMENDOUS SIGNIFICANCE. NEVER UNDERESTIMATE THE POWER OF A SKY FULL OF STARS, THE IMPORTANCE OF A HUG, OR LETTING NATURE SHARE ITS WISDOM.

- LIVE FEARLESSLY. THERE IS NO SUCH THING AS FAILURE, ONLY VALUABLE LESSONS.

- TRUST YOUR INSTINCTS TO GUIDE YOU. IT IS YOUR INTERNAL COMPASS AND YOUR GREATEST PROTECTOR.

- DO ACTIVITIES THAT MAKE YOUR SOUL SING. DANCE. CREATE. PLAY GAMES. PAINT PICTURES. IF YOU'RE TOO BUSY TO HAVE FUN OR DO THE THINGS YOU ENJOY, CONSIDER ALLOCATING YOUR TIME DIFFERENTLY.

- LIFE IS TERMINAL. THE DAY WE ARE BORN, WE START THE PROCESS OF DYING. WHETHER YOU HAVE BEEN DIAGNOSED WITH A LIFE-THREATENING ILLNESS OR NOT, LIFE IS NOT PERMANENT. LIVE EACH MOMENT TO THE FULLEST. MAKE EACH SECOND COUNT. EACH DAY, DO SOMETHING POSITIVE

THAT WILL HELP NOT ONLY YOUR FUTURE SELF BUT THE
FUTURE OF OTHERS.

- BREAK FREE FROM THE "ACT" AND EMBRACE THE "ART OF
  LIVING."

- LET YOUR LIFE PURPOSE DRIVE YOU. IF YOU'RE UNSURE OF
  WHAT IT IS, THE ANSWER WILL APPEAR WHEN YOU'RE READY
  TO EMBRACE IT.

- THERE IS A LEVEL OF LOVE THAT WORDS CANNOT DESCRIBE. IF
  YOU'VE NEVER HAD THE OPPORTUNITY TO EXPERIENCE ITS
  POWER, YOU WILL. WHEN YOU DO, IT WILL PUT YOUR ENTIRE
  EXISTENCE INTO PERSPECTIVE. WE ARE MADE FROM LOVE; WE
  LIVE FOR LOVE; WE ARE LOVE.

- FREE YOUR MIND FROM RESTRICTIVE THOUGHTS. YOU CAN DO
  ANYTHING. MAKE ANYTHING. BE ANYTHING.

- AND FINALLY, ON YOUR WORST DAYS, REMEMBER THAT A
  CANCER PATIENT IS SITTING IN A CHEMO ROOM OR RADIATION
  FACILITY, FIGHTING FOR A FUTURE. LIFE ISN'T EASY, BUT YOU
  ARE BLESSED TO BE ALIVE. EVERY DAY, GOOD OR BAD, IS
  WORTH LIVING.

* * *

Remember, every moment is special, significant, and intertwined.
Own the now.

AFTERWORD

Pathology results confirmed I was diagnosed with Invasive Ductal Carcinoma, node-negative, triple-positive, stage 2A breast cancer (the tumor was 2-5 centimeters in size without lymph node involvement).

On May 5, 2018, I handed David a tissue to dry his tears when he saw my sister walk down the aisle in her stunning 'Casablanca' bridal gown, the crystals reflecting the glorious Jamaican sun. To hear them say, "I do," was an unforgettable moment, worth the fight to get there.

Shortly after, a lump appeared on the right side of my neck. Terrified cancer had returned, I immediately went to see Dr. Santos, who referred me to an oncologist specializing in neck cancers. It took five anxiety-ridden days to get the biopsy results back, but with deep gratitude, it was benign.

On June 4, I finished my monoclonal antibody therapy infusions. My port was removed ten days later during a simple in-office procedure. A half-inch scar, where the implant once was, is now a tiny badge of honor.

On August 2, 2018, Bruce's brother, Bob, passed away from

colon cancer that had spread to his lungs. "I fought like a mother-fucker," he told us over the phone a few days before he died. And he had. His fight against cancer is what I respected him for the most.

Although Uncle Gary's efforts to "slay the dragon" were fierce, in February 2020, he passed away from cancer, too. We traveled back to Nebraska to join the Wells family in celebrating his life. A set of hand-whittled, wooden toy cars sat next to photos and flowers, displaying his legacy.

Anjelica and her mom held a reunion for *The Radiation Club* in their backyard. I invited Bruce to join me. Everyone in the club attended, and we sat around a long table, our feet nestled in the cool grass, eating grilled salmon and reminiscing about our time together. On our drive home that night, Bruce said, "There aren't many times in life where you meet a group of strangers who immediately feel like friends." He summed up *The Club* perfectly.

Life (post-cancer) isn't easy, although I feel extremely grateful to know what it feels like to be cancer-free again. It took me a year to run my fingers through my hair without the fear of it pulling out. When memories feel heavy, I take a few deep breaths and remind myself to stay in the present. *Treat each day as its own.*

I've held on to the souvenirs I collected during my journey. A linen bag containing the ponytail Bruce shaved off my head is still stuffed into the bottom drawer of my credenza, next to my weathered ball cap. I've kept every letter, every card, and every gift given to me by THE SECRET SOCIETY.

With Stella by my side, Bruce finally took my portrait by the "Cancer Survivors Park" sign. We strolled through the park for the first time, admiring the colorful flowers and tiny waterfall that fell over layers of rock while reading inspiring quotes.

Does the possibility of a recurrence still enter my mind?

All. The. Time.

When I feel a sharp pain anywhere in my body, my mind leaps

to cancer. Although I am diligent about clinical breast exams, mammograms, and self-checks, the fear has still not subsided. I'm not sure if it ever will. Healing takes time, and as long as I have time, my healing journey continues.

One superhero said, "Post-cancer is like having a loaded gun pointed at my back. At any point, the trigger may be pulled. So, I live on edge, always waiting for what might happen." I, too, have a loaded gun pointed at my back, but I use it as a reminder to never take a second of life for granted.

In all the ways the cancer journey changed me, my approach to life is what I am the proudest of. When my mind gets charged with fear, anxiety, or overthinking, I place the palm of my right hand over my heart. Everything that matters resides there. Love will, and always has, carried me through. As I close my eyes, I remind myself, "You are alive; live fearlessly."

MEDICAL TIMELINE (REFERENCE ONLY)

2016

- July - Annual Physical with Primary Doctor
- July 14 - First Mammogram, No Evidence of Disease

2017

- April 4 - Sneezing Attack, Muscle Strain
- April 9 - Lump Discovered in Right Breast, Emailed Primary Doctor
- April 13 - Appointment with Primary Doctor, Second Mammogram in Right Breast
- April 28 - Ultrasound Guided Core Biopsy
- May 1 - Diagnosed with Invasive Ductal Carcinoma (Breast Cancer)
- May 4 - Targeted Mammogram in Right Breast
- May 10 - Ultrasound in Left Breast, Stereotactic Breast Biopsy in Right Breast

- MAY 11 - APPOINTMENT WITH SURGEON, MET WITH CANCER CARE COORDINATOR
- MAY 22 - APPOINTMENT WITH ONCOLOGIST
- MAY 25 - GENETIC COUNSELOR MEETING, ORIENTATION TO CHEMOTHERAPY
- MAY 30 - MUGA HEART SCAN 1 OF 5 (FOR HERCEPTIN INFUSION)
- JUNE 2 - PORT IMPLANT SURGERY
- JUNE 6 - CHEMOTHERAPY TREATMENT 1 OF 6
- JUNE 13 - GENETIC TEST RESULTS
- JUNE 21 - FOLLOW-UP WITH ONCOLOGIST, BREAST MRI
- JUNE 27 - CHEMOTHERAPY TREATMENT 2 OF 6
- JULY 1 - BREAST MRI RESULTS
- JULY 18 - CHEMOTHERAPY TREATMENT 3 OF 6
- AUGUST 8 - CHEMOTHERAPY TREATMENT 4 OF 6
- AUGUST 28 - MUGA HEART SCAN 2 OF 5 (FOR HERCEPTIN INFUSION)
- AUGUST 29 - CHEMOTHERAPY TREATMENT 5 OF 6
- SEPTEMBER 18 - FOLLOW-UP WITH SURGEON
- SEPTEMBER 19 - CHEMOTHERAPY TREATMENT 6 OF 6
- OCTOBER 5 - FOLLOW-UP WITH ONCOLOGIST, ULTRASOUND ON RIGHT BREAST
- OCTOBER 10 - MONOCLONAL ANTIBODY THERAPY INFUSION 1 OF 12
- OCTOBER 11 - PRE-OP WITH SURGEON
- OCTOBER 25 - LUMPECTOMY (BREAST CONSERVING SURGERY) FOR RIGHT BREAST
- OCTOBER 31 - MONOCLONAL ANTIBODY THERAPY INFUSION 2 OF 12
- NOVEMBER 2 - FOLLOW UP WITH SURGEON, NO CANCER FOUND
- NOVEMBER 8 - APPOINTMENT WITH RADIATION ONCOLOGIST

- November 20 - Follow-Up with Oncologist, Start Tamoxifen
- November 21 - Appointment in Radiology to Prepare and Monoclonal Antibody Therapy Infusion 3 of 12
- November 30 - Appointment in Radiology to Prepare
- December 4 - Radiation Therapy 1 of 20
- December 5 - Radiation Therapy 2 of 20
- December 6 - Radiation Therapy 3 of 20
- December 7 - Radiation Therapy 4 of 20
- December 8 - Radiation Therapy 5 of 20
- December 11 - Radiation Therapy 6 of 20
- December 12 - Radiation Therapy 7 of 20, Monoclonal Antibody Therapy Infusion 4 of 12
- December 13 - Radiation Therapy 8 of 20
- December 14 - Radiation Therapy 9 of 20, MUGA Heart Scan 3 of 5
- December 15 - Radiation Therapy 10 of 20
- December 18 - Radiation Therapy 11 of 20
- December 19 - Radiation Therapy 12 of 20
- December 20 - Radiation Therapy 13 of 20
- December 21 - Radiation Therapy 14 of 20
- December 22 - Radiation Therapy 15 of 20
- December 26 - Radiation Therapy 16 of 20
- December 27 - Radiation Therapy 17 of 20
- December 28 - Radiation Therapy 18 of 20
- December 29 - Radiation Therapy 19 of 20

2018

- January 2 - Radiation Therapy 20 of 20, Monoclonal Antibody Therapy Infusion 5 of 12
- January 16 - Follow-Up with Oncologist

- JANUARY 23 - MONOCLONAL ANTIBODY THERAPY INFUSION 6 OF 12
- FEBRUARY 12 - MONOCLONAL ANTIBODY THERAPY INFUSION 7 OF 12
- MARCH 3 - MUGA HEART SCAN 4 OF 5 (FOR HERCEPTIN INFUSION)
- MARCH 5 - MONOCLONAL ANTIBODY THERAPY INFUSION 8 OF 12
- MARCH 26 - MONOCLONAL ANTIBODY THERAPY INFUSION 9 OF 12
- APRIL 16 - MONOCLONAL ANTIBODY THERAPY INFUSION 10 OF 12
- MAY 15 - MONOCLONAL ANTIBODY THERAPY INFUSION 11 OF 12
- MAY 24 - MUGA HEART SCAN 5 OF 5 (FOR HERCEPTIN INFUSION)
- JUNE 4 - MONOCLONAL ANTIBODY THERAPY INFUSION 12 OF 12
- JUNE 14 - PORT REMOVAL SURGERY

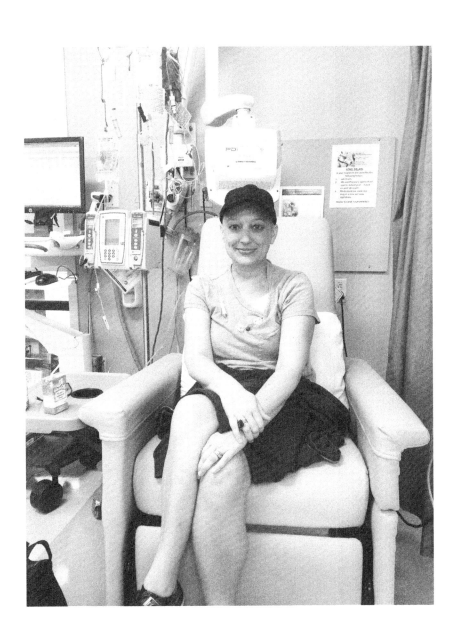

HEALING LIGHT MEDITATION

Welcome, my friends, to the *Healing Light Meditation*. I created this meditation to support my body in healing from cancer. It helped with pain management, silenced the anxiety, and provided the peaceful space my body needed to overcome.

I invite you to try this meditation by reading through it and committing the concept to memory or visit www.feistyrighty.com where there is a free audio recording. If you'd like to customize the meditation to make it your own, please do.

Enjoy the *Healing Light Meditation*.

* * *

Please get comfortable, preferably lying down on your back. If you need to sit up, that's okay, too. Close your eyes and take several deep breaths, inhaling and exhaling slowly. Just be present in your body.

Now acknowledge how your body feels. Notice any discomfort or sensations without judgment. Continue to take deep, cleansing breaths.

In your mind's eye, picture a soothing color hovering over your head. It can be any soothing color. Notice its tone and intensity. This color will be your healing light for today.

With a few deep breaths, give the light permission to flow gently into your body through the top of your head. Feel its presence as it removes negative thoughts. If your mind starts to drift, simply return your focus to the beautiful healing light.

Allow the purifying light to move down into your chest, filling the space around your heart. Let it rest there as you feel its nurturing love.

Allow the light to split and flow down each arm to your fingertips. Open your palms and let the healing light rest in your hands. You hold its incredible power. Let the light rest there.

The light reunites in your belly. Feel its warmth, still focusing on the light's color. Take several deep breaths, inhaling and exhaling slowly.

As the color once again divides, the grounding and healing light flows down each thigh, past your knees, and down into your feet. It reminds you that you belong here, on earth, in your body, and are one with all living things. Breathe in the beauty of life, and exhale thoughts that no longer serve you. Let the light gently rest at your feet.

Now that your entire body has experienced this miraculous light, redirect it to the area of your body that needs the most attention. It may be an area of discomfort or a place in your body where illness resides. Allow the light to become brighter in the area that needs healing.

The light is never too warm or overpowering; it is simply the perfect temperature for your body. Let the healing light permeate the area as its intensity brightens. It purifies your body in real-time, supports your immune system, and grants you the ability to play an essential role in your healing. Feel gratitude towards the light and its ability to help heal you.

Be with the light and allow some time to pass.

Remember that the light is a gift you can access anytime. This meditation is an act of self-love. You are actively giving your body the space and permission to heal.

When ready, take a few more deep breaths and open your eyes.

Namaste.

ACKNOWLEDGMENTS

I am forever grateful to my sister, Christine, for her guidance, expertise, and incredible insight as a writer. Thank you for mentoring me and encouraging me to be brave enough to write from the heart.

Bruce, thank you for wholeheartedly believing in this project enough to put our lives on hold so I could spend time writing.

A special thank you to my mother, Mary, for the profound wisdom, endless support, insight, and belief in this book from the beginning.

Courtney Keller, thanks for using your incredible talent to create a book cover that perfectly illustrates the concept.

I'm grateful to the editorial and production team who helped strengthen this book: Christine Conradt, Patricia Malin, Mary Conradt, Kit Keller, Sean Gannon, and Elizabeth Shotkoski. Your input was invaluable.

With endless love and gratitude, I'd like to thank THE SECRET SOCIETY: Bruce, Mary, Chris, David, Jerry, Betty, Mae, Utaiwan, Lily, Beth, Ozzy, Ralph, Patricia, Carolyn, Sandi, Chad, Tammy, Pam, and Marilyn. And, of course, Stella, my dog.

Special thanks to *The Radiation Club:* Jelsma, Mr. and Mrs. Garza, Bobby, Paige, Henry, Joseph, Margaret, Shirley, Jules, Anjelica, and Kindra. I am grateful for your support and friendship.

To the breast cancer patients (peers) I had the honor to mentor during the past four years while working on this book, thank you for allowing me to share some of my stories with you during our one-on-one conversations. Your reactions and responses were inspiring and significant.

And to the medical teams, doctors, nurses, and researchers who dedicate their work to making a patient's life better, I applaud you. And most of all, from the depths of my soul, I thank you.

ABOUT THE AUTHOR

Jennifer D. James is an author, cancer survivor, trained breast cancer mentor through the American Cancer Society, certified meditation teacher specializing in patient healing and pain management, certified Maurer Foundation breast health educator, and advocate for individuals diagnosed with cancer to help them gain necessary resources. By sharing her journey, she hopes to encourage women to schedule routine breast screenings while opening the conversation about cancer to shift the narrative. Jennifer currently resides in Palm Springs, California, with her husband, Bruce.

Visit Jennifer D. James online at www.feistyrighty.com.

- Facebook: Feisty Righty
- Instagram: @feistyrighty
- TikTok: @feistyrighty

PLEASE SPREAD THE WORD

Book reviews help create a strong online presence, which translates into accessibility. This memoir was created with the intent to empower and support individuals diagnosed with breast cancer along with their caregivers. The more people reached, the more support can be given.

To help us achieve our goal, **please consider leaving a review about *Feisty Righty* at your regular Ebookstore.**

Together, we can make a difference, open the conversation about cancer, and shift the narrative worldwide.

Made in the USA
Monee, IL
07 July 2023

38556266R00194